THE SEVEN CHALLENGES® MANUAL

Robert Schwebel, Ph.D.

ISBN 1-890164-22-4

This manual has been written to help practitioners understand The Seven Challenges®; its clinical approaches, published materials, and implementation issues. Organizations and practitioners cannot implement The Seven Challenges Program or announce that they are providing the program without training and authorization from The Seven Challenges, LLC.

For information regarding implementation of The Seven Challenges® Program, please contact Sharon Conner by email at sconner@sevenchallenges.com or by telephone at (520) 405-4559.

DEDICATION

This book is dedicated to Claudia, my wife and partner in creating The Seven Challenges, to our children Frank and Henry, and to all adults who want to make a better world for children.

ACKNOWLEDGEMENTS

I want to thank Randy Muck from Center for Substance Abuse Treatment (CSAT) for strongly encouraging me to write this manual, and Jutta Butler, also from CSAT, who said it had to be done. Thanks to Jeff Kaplan who has provided thoughtful and supportive feedback to me about the program and to Richard Barr and Douglas C. Smith for their ideas about training and monitoring. Thanks to Jay Zaslaw who has supported The Seven Challenges and contributed valuable ideas about working with probation, and in drug court and juvenile correctional settings. Dave Lazarus from GroundZero Design deserves recognition for his creative contributions and design of Seven Challenges materials. I remain grateful to Fletcher McCusker who early on recognized the merit of this program and supported it, and to Tom Rose who told me to keep trying to make the program easy to use. Thanks to my father who provided extraordinary editorial help and my mother who taught me to work hard — always — and to both of them who said it is important to make a contribution to the world. Many of the ideas in this manual were inspired by people who participated in training sessions across the country, and now beyond. I thank all of you.

ABOUT THIS MANUAL

The idea of manualizing treatment is appealing because it helps ensure fidelity of treatment – that is, that counselors are delivering the intended approach to clients. Manuals offer a careful description of how to implement and conduct a certain approach to counseling. They serve as a good training resource. They spell out the techniques to be employed and how to implement them. Manualizing also benefits researchers who can feel confident that they are studying a unitary approach to treatment that has some degree of consistency across practitioners. The ideal outcome of research is validated technology – identifying effective programs that can be replicated. Clients, providers, and payers want to be confident that a treatment approach works.

One problem with manualizing is that the counseling process involves a specialized, interpersonal relationship that cannot be translated into simple mechanics. When counseling is manualized to the point of telling counselors what to say and do at each session, it provides standardization and consistency, but at an enormous cost. Good counseling must be responsive to clients' needs, emotions, and thought processes. Too much is compromised or lost when the whole process is rigidly guided by pre-determined protocol.

This manual has been written to help practitioners implement The Seven Challenges® Program with great confidence in the fidelity of their treatment. It is designed to supplement, but not replace Seven Challenges® Training. The manual spells out in clear detail the philosophy and strategy of the program. It explains the health decision-making process inherent in The Seven Challenges, and clarifies the meaning of each of the challenges. It presents the basic Seven Challenges Counseling Approaches. It explains how to introduce and orient youth to The Seven Challenges Program, and how to use Seven Challenges materials, including *The Seven Challenges* book, and the nine *Seven Challenges Journals*. It explains how to give feedback to help young people in journaling, one of the important elements of the program. Further, it defines "working sessions" in adolescent drug treatment, explaining how to avoid widely-played games — such as "Try to make me quit" or "Try to prove that I've been harmed by drugs" and other variations of these games – all of which are wasteful diversions from meaningful work.

This manual offers model statements about how to introduce and discuss various issues. It suggests ideas about content for group sessions. It discusses some of the nuts and bolts of the program such as settings in which it can be used, time requirements, types of groups, size of groups, length of group sessions, composition of groups, issues related to individual and family sessions, and more. It examines important group start-up issues, such as how to "win group consciousness." It presents material about helping clients who are required to be drug free (perhaps by courts or schools), but may not be ready to successfully become drug free. It also provides help to supervisors in terms of issues that frequently arise in implementing the program. However, this manual does *not* micro-manage what counselors say and do on a daily basis. Rather it provides the framework for implementing the Seven Challenges Program, with help and guidelines for use of the materials and for the counseling sessions. But the counseling must be personalized and individualized. Counseling is different from psycho-educational sessions that can be fully prescribed, and from the implementation of a program of rigid, mandated protocols.

With this manual and training in The Seven Challenges, counselors can get a good start on delivering The Seven Challenges Program in an effective way. Not everyone, however, will be doing the exact same thing each day. The program requires individual initiative by counselors, and draws upon their clinical skills. It also requires that counselors incorporate some distinct techniques that can add to their repertoire of skills. These skills are not mastered in one training session or by reading a manual. They are cultivated and refined over years of experience. Complemented by training, this manual will help get people started in delivering effective Seven Challenges drug counseling services to youth.

Robert Schwebel, Ph.D.
Tucson, Arizona
April 2004

Table of Contents

Table of Contents

INTRODUCTION TO THE SEVEN CHALLENGES

PURPOSE OF THE PROGRAM

The Seven Challenges® Program is designed for adolescent (and young adult) substance abusing and substance dependent individuals to motivate decisions and commitments to change. Once such decisions and commitments are made, the program guides young people toward success in implementing the desired changes.

START WHERE YOUTH ARE "AT"

Although we might wish that young people would enter treatment eager and ready to quit using drugs, most come under duress, often dragged in by parents, schools, the courts, or the juvenile correctional system. We have to begin where the young people are "at" (usually resistant and reluctant to change) not where we wish they might be, or might pretend to be (fully and honestly prepared to quit using drugs).

TRUST AND RELATIONSHIP-BUILDING COME FIRST

The Seven Challenges is a relationship-based program. Counselors start with an under-standing that young people generally come to treatment against their will, or at best with little enthusiasm about the experience. Many youth are accustomed to lying to adults. They are also accustomed to being around adults with whom, if they told the truth, they would only get into more trouble. Most youth expect that counselors will try to control them and make them quit using drugs. Some may have had previous negative experiences in treatment. Many may be quite angry or defensive about these experiences. Unless counselors proactively address this negative expectation about counseling, most young people will remain predisposed to resisting adults or "faking it." With The Seven Challenges, trust and relationship building come first, and remain important issues throughout the program. Our aim is to create a climate in which young people feel safe to talk openly and honestly about themselves and their drug use. Unless trust is built in a counseling relationship, there will be little likelihood of positive outcomes. Good relationships lead to retention in counseling, and retention correlates with success.[1] We also know that many young people in drug treatment come from high-risk environments. Forming relationships with an adult who cares is one of the key predictors of resilience. That is, youth who connect with adults who care about them are much more likely to fare well than those who do not.[2]

SUPPORT ADOLESCENT DEVELOPMENT

Adolescents need developmentally appropriate drug treatment. During the adolescent stage of life, young people are faced with the developmental tasks of defining their own independent identities, learning systematic logical thinking, and preparing for adult roles. It makes little sense to try to dictate and control their behavior. Most youth would simply rebel. Instead, adults should help young people learn to make their own wise decisions. We need to help them develop logical abilities, and then apply these thinking skills to their lives. Because we live in a drug-filled society, when young people forge independent identities and prepare for the future, they must determine where they stand in relationship to drugs. This is an inescapable challenge. The Seven Challenges Program gives young people an opportunity to do this – a chance to think about the impact of their drug use upon their current lives, and its potential impact upon what lies ahead in adulthood. In that way, we work with development, rather than against it.

COGNITIVE/EMOTIONAL DECISION-MAKING MODEL

As trust builds in the counseling setting, the Seven Challenges Program helps young people look at their lives and consider where their drug use fits with what has happened in the past, what is happening now, and what they would like to see happen in their future. Counselors help youth through the difficult and sometimes lengthy process of thinking through drug and lifestyle decisions for themselves.

Young people consider:

- why they are using drugs

- what they like about drugs

- how they harm themselves and others by using drugs

- how their continued use might affect their future if they do not change.

Humans do not want to be controlled. Research about psychological reactance[3] has confirmed that no one wants to be backed into the corner and forced to behave in certain ways. People need to feel that they have choices. When backed into corners, they get defensive and attempt to assert their liberty. ("I'll show you: No one tells me what to do.") The urge toward self-determination is especially acute in adolescents who are developmentally charged with forming independent identities. Young clients need an opportunity to make their own informed choices.

The Seven Challenges incorporates a cognitive/emotional, decision-making process. The program does not attempt to dictate behavior or coerce young people. Rather it helps them learn to think for themselves, consider all relevant information, and then make their own wise decisions. Relevant information includes awareness of the emotional issues that influence human decision-making – the emotions we may seek and those we want to avoid or minimize.[4] With adolescents in particular, it is important to show confidence in their competency and to support their sense of self-efficacy, as in "You can do it."[5]

THE HEALTH DECISION-MAKING MODEL

In the Seven Challenges Program, young people are given an opportunity to reflect upon their drug using behavior within the framework of a health decision-making model.

Using drugs or not — and the extent of drug use by those who indulge — are health decisions. People are deciding what they choose to put in their bodies. Drug use has important implications for physical and emotional health.

People make health decisions by weighing the "costs" versus the "benefits" of the behavior under consideration. We do this, for example, when we decide whether or not to wear seat belts: On the one hand, seatbelts are cumbersome and uncomfortable, and rarely needed. On the other hand, they are required by law and can be life-saving in an accident. (In fact, 75% of the population use their seat belts regularly.) Another example of a health decision is about eating "junk food," which is high in calories, fat, and cholesterol, but may taste good, be readily available, and have great mouth feel. People compare the relative value of the benefits and the costs. Similarly, people make health decisions about drugs. They weigh what they like about drugs (the benefits) against the harm and potential harm (the costs).

Clear, informed thinking is required for good decision-making. This type of thinking is not likely to take place in contentious relationships in which people are arguing with one another. Too often drug treatment of adolescents can degenerate into a battle of wills with counselors trying to convince their young clients to quit, and the clients defending their drug use. That is one reason why relationship building is a crucial priority in The Seven Challenges.

HOLISTIC VISION

Drug use is not a stand-alone, peripheral behavior in an adolescent's life. People use drugs for a reason – to try to satisfy personal desires and needs. A holistic program not only must address the drug use, but also the reasons for "using." In The Seven Challenges Program, young people identify the desires and needs they are satisfying, or attempting to satisfy, through their drug use. They may be using alcohol and other drugs to avoid or cope with stress, tension, boredom, anxiety, fear or other feelings. They may use them to moderate their anger or release it, or to "self medicate" against negative emotions. Young people sometimes use drugs to temporarily forget painful life experiences, such as child abuse or other trauma, or to silence self-doubts or self-deprecating thoughts. Sometimes drugs are used to escape from reality instead of facing it — or to quell various uncomfortable feelings. Sometimes drugs are used simply for pleasure or fun.

When self understanding increases – when young people see why they are using drugs – they have an opportunity to think about alternatives to drug use. They can learn healthy, drug-free ways to meet these same needs and satisfy desires. One way to tip the balance toward healthier decisions about using drugs is to provide healthy, drug-free options.

AN EMPOWERMENT MODEL: SOLVING CO-OCCURRING PROBLEMS AND TEACHING LIFE SKILLS

The Seven Challenges Program does not narrowly focus on drug seeking and drug taking behavior. It goes further and provides young people with an opportunity to identify and solve co-occurring, underlying psychological problems that motivate their drug use. This includes supporting them in their efforts at resolving trauma issues. Co-occurring problems are the norm with drug abuse, and these problems must be addressed in a comprehensive drug treatment program.

The Seven Challenges also places a strong emphasis on teaching social, psychological and emotional life skills, so that individuals can learn new, positive ways to cope with life, meet their needs, and satisfy their desires. In the program, young people learn problem solving skills, communication skills, anger management skills, social/relationship skills, self-control skills, thinking skills, and relaxation and stress reduction skills. Clients are given opportunities to resolve trauma issues and overcome a variety of psychological problems that may plague them.[6]

Solving co-occurring problems and learning life skills empowers young people to meet their needs in healthy ways, without drugs. It puts them in a position from which they could choose, of their own accord, to give up drugs, but still have other ways to attain satisfaction, pleasure, and happiness in life.

REDEFINING THE ROLE OF THE DRUG COUNSELOR

Young people who believe that counselors are striving *to make them* quit using drugs will see counselors as antagonists. They will see counselors as trying to take something away from them – their drugs. Drugs may be the only way some young people can envision satisfying their own needs. *Counselors in The Seven Challenges Program must redefine their role. "We are not here to take something away. We are on your side. We are your problem-solving partners. We're here to help you think about your options and to give you more options. When you have learned new ways to meet your needs and considered your options, you may choose – of your own accord – to give up drugs. But that will be for you to decide."*

INSPIRING HOPE

People don't make changes in their lives if they think their lives will get worse. They make changes when they believe that their lives would improve. That is why it is so important to empower young people to feel that if they choose to give up drugs, they will have better lives. They would be giving up the benefits they derive from drug use. In exchange, however, they would stop the physical, psychological, and social harm caused by drugs, and find other ways to satisfy their personal needs.

By way of illustration:

- A person who is seriously depressed and uses drugs to self medicate is unlikely to choose to quit using unless there is some hope of overcoming the depression. Without this hope, quitting drugs would be seen as stopping the harm from the drugs, but leaving this person feeling miserable.

- A person who has a serious anger problem, uses drugs to moderate the anger, and is frightened of being explosive when not self-medicating would be quite reluctant to choose to stop using drugs unless: (1) this person acquired skill in problem solving (to prevent angry situations from occurring); or (2) learned other ways to manage the anger; or (3) knew he or she would have an opportunity to learn anger management skills in the near future.

- Victims of physical or sexual abuse who self medicate with drugs would be reluctant to quit using drugs unless they felt they could resolve the trauma and cope with their thoughts and feelings about it.

People such as those described above, who feel pessimistic or hopeless about their future, need to believe that things could get better before they would be willing to stop coping the way they have been coping — by using drugs.

Many young people who abuse drugs have already been discouraged about life and may have a sense of powerlessness and hopelessness. The Seven Challenges promotes and teaches skills to create a better life, but also works to promote optimism and hope. This includes conveying a sense of personal power – that people can make changes and make their lives better. This sense of optimism is reinforced as young people are empowered to learn various life skills in The Seven Challenges Program.

THINKING ABOUT CHANGE

After young people reflect upon their lives, including their use of drugs, The Seven Challenges Program offers them an opportunity to think about making changes:

- what it takes to change

- what they might gain and lose by changing

- which changes they might want to make

- how they would go about making such changes

- what they need to do so they feel that they could successfully make the desired changes

We know that most young people do not enter drug programs wanting to change, ready to change, or even able to change their drug use behavior. They are in the earlier stages of the change process. First they need to recognize the problem, then consider making changes, then make decisions about changing, then prepare to change, and finally, make the desired changes. Important psychological research by Prochaska, Norcross and DiClemente[7] has identified six stages of change in overcoming problem behaviors – and discussed the implications of their findings in terms of matching appropriate interventions to an individual's particular stage. The application of the stages of change research to work with adolescent substance abusing youth is discussed in more detail later in this manual (pages 26-28). The Seven Challenges Program is designed to match the intervention to the clients' stages of change.

BEHAVIORAL SUCCESS

When young people make decisions and set goals for themselves (about their drug use or their lives), they need help and support in initiating and maintaining new behavior. The Seven Challenges Program supports them and guides them toward successful implementation of the changes they pursue.

The Seven Challenges Program provides Lifestyle Action Groups (see Seven Challenges Services, pages 83-84) for young people who are committed to making changes in their lives. These groups are focused on following through on decisions. In the groups, young people get support in making any behavior changes they have chosen to make – such as learning anger management, learning to cope with stress in positive ways, etc. For those who commit to stopping their use of alcohol and other drugs, a specialized part of the Lifestyle Action Group teaches state of the art relapse prevention skills, which is incorporated in work in Challenges Six and Seven.

When youth have decided to become drug free, individuals and agencies that implement The Seven Challenges may want to use community resources such as 12-steps programs, Smart Recovery, or other recovery groups to supplement Seven Challenges work. Appropriate support should be available to all youth who want to overcome problems of drug abuse and drug dependence. Spiritually minded youth who accept the ideas of (1) admitting powerlessness over their drug use and (2) surrendering to a higher power should be encouraged to attend 12 step groups.

Until recently, drug treatment tended to be defined as either pro 12-steps, or against it. The Seven Challenges offers a different perspective. Whereas a 12-step program is designed for people who are motivated to make significant changes in their lives, we know that most youth enter drug treatment in the very early stages of change. Most are far from ready to make informed, internally motivated, and committed decisions to quit using drugs, and are poorly prepared to succeed even if they were to make such decisions. The Seven Challenges starts working with youth in these earlier stages. It is only after considerable effort and significant progress has been made that young clients are ready to swing into the action stage. Although The Seven Challenges is not a 12-step program, it is not opposed to it. When young people are ready to stop using drugs, 12-step programs are one of a number of viable options for additional support. Youth in The Seven Challenges Program who want to take the spiritual approach to maintaining abstinence should have access to 12-step groups. Other youth should be oriented to the 12-steps, whether they accept the principles of it or not, because it is a universally available support group in their communities.

CULTURAL AND GENDER ISSUES

The Seven Challenges Program and materials were developed while working with – and with the input of – a culturally diverse group of youth. An effort has been made to put substance abuse in a social and cultural context. People use drugs, at least in part, in response to their circumstances and environment. The Seven Challenges

Program is designed to help young people understand and explore the context of their drug use. Often, serious environmental risk factors correlate with drug use (for example: child abuse and other trauma, poverty, and families experiencing high levels of stress). Clients need help in understanding this. By teaching life skills and encouraging positive relationships, the program builds resilience within clients to cope with these stressors, and offers an opportunity to strengthen and reinforce protective factors.

The Seven Challenges Program was developed in clinical settings with both boys and girls. As such, it could be considered gender neutral, with both sexes equally represented. However, there are special considerations when using this program with either sex. Gender responsive considerations are discussed later in this manual (pages 137-145).

PUBLISHED
MATERIALS

BOOKS, JOURNALS, AND OTHER PRINTED MATERIAL

The Seven Challenges Program incorporates the use of the 120-page book, *The Seven Challenges*, which is a collection of readings for youth; the nine *Seven Challenges Journals* designed for counselor/youth interaction; The Seven Challenges Poster; and The Seven Challenges Diplomas. Resources for counselors include the books: *The Seven Challenges Activity Book* and this publication, *The Seven Challenges Manual*. A variety of other printed materials have also been developed to assist in implementation of the program, such as a sample treatment note, a list of treatment goals, and information about implementation in different settings.

The Seven Challenges and the nine *Seven Challenges Journals* are available in Spanish. They were translated by a native Spanish speaker, in collaboration with the author of the program to ensure fidelity of meaning.

Explanations about the use of this printed material are included in this manual. Seven Challenges® Training is required to maximize benefits of the published material, to fully implement the program, and for an individual or agency to announce that they are doing The Seven Challenges® Program.

METHODS

　　The Seven Challenges Manual　©2004 Robert Schwebel, Ph.D.

CORE COMPONENTS

Youth are guided through The Seven Challenges Program by a combination of:

- Readings in *The Seven Challenges*
- "Journaling" in the *Seven Challenges Journals*
- Educational/counseling sessions in one-to-one and/or group settings
- Family or multi/family sessions, when feasible and appropriate

To successfully implement the program, staff must be thoroughly familiar with The Seven Challenges published material; know how to introduce the program and the materials to youth; know how to give feedback to youth who write in the journals; know how to promote openness and talk with, or counsel, young people to empower them, without eliciting defensiveness and without getting hooked into power struggles; and be able to integrate the topics or content of counseling sessions with The Seven Challenges process. They must be prepared to work in a holistic manner with youth. On the one hand, this means being informed by a basic understanding of drug information (widely available elsewhere; not included in this manual).[8] On the other hand, this means being able to teach problem solving skills and various life skills, which are also essential to this program.

The extent to which the *full* power of this program is utilized will depend to a large extent on the clinical skills of those who use it. Among these are specialized Seven Challenges Counseling Approaches that maximize impact of The Seven Challenges Program. These approaches are introduced in this handbook, and taught in Seven Challenges Trainings®.

The Seven Challenges Program has been implemented in a wide array of treatment settings (outpatient, intensive outpatient, inpatient, residential, day treatment, partial care programs, and in-home). It has also been used in public and private schools, juvenile probation departments, and public and private correctional facilities.

READINGS

The Seven Challenges reader is based on the experiences of young people who have been successful in overcoming alcohol and other drug problems. (This is why the text is written in the first person plural – We – format.) This book of readings expresses their point of view. What these youth had in common was that they all were willing to *challenge* themselves to think honestly about their lives and their use of drugs. That is why the book and the program are called The Seven Challenges. Readings are an important part of the program, providing ideas and inspiration to help young people look at their own lives. The book is divided into seven chapters, one for each challenge. This book and other materials are all written in very simple, easy-to-read language.

JOURNALS

The Seven Challenges Journals are a valuable and powerful tool to help young people look at their lives and drug use, to support them in making important decisions about their future, and in following through with positive changes in their lives. Young people write in the nine journals, one at a time, and receive extensive feedback from counselors. When youth have answered all questions in a journal, they pass them to their counselors who read the journal and respond with their own comments. Each journal goes back and forth between the client and counselor several times before the client completes it and moves on to the next journal. Through the journaling, a special type of relationship and communication develops between youth and their counselors. Often young people will write down thoughts and feelings, and share experiences, they might be reluctant to disclose in face-to-face conversations.

There are nine journals in the program. Because of the sheer volume of material in Challenge One, this challenge has been divided into two separate publications – Challenge One: Part One and Challenge One: Part Two. Because youth are asked to make decisions about both lifestyle and drug issues in this program, Challenge Seven is divided into two parts as well. Part One concerns follow up on lifestyle decisions. Part Two concerns follow up on drug decisions.

COUNSELING / EDUCATIONAL SESSIONS

Young people with drug problems need to "talk it out" in counseling/educational sessions as they examine their lives and consider making changes. There is no pre-set agenda for counseling/educational sessions in The Seven Challenges Program, nor are there scripted sessions. Good drug counseling must be responsive to the interests and needs of youth, and their current realities. Effectiveness is seriously compromised in pre-scripted, one-size-fits-all programs. Therefore, counselors must plan sessions according to the needs of individual clients at any given time. Although not pre-scripted, the content of each and every counseling session should be integrated in such a way that young people can see how their efforts relate to helping them through the decision making process using The Seven Challenges Process. (How to skillfully do this will be discussed later in this manual, on pages 75-76.) It is also important that counseling sessions are all "working sessions" – not a time for game playing and ceaseless argumentation (pages 127-135).

Counselors provide leadership at counseling sessions by pursuing discussions on important issues relevant to youth or initiating activities that promote thinking about relevant issues, or by teaching important life skills. This requires awareness of which issues to focus on – and when. It requires attentiveness to individual or group needs, and responsiveness to youth concerns. Co-occurring problems need to be addressed in counseling sessions. Some counselors with a background in drug counseling do not feel prepared to help with mental health issues. The program materials help with this. But these counselors may want to broaden their own training, or work on teams with other counselors with a broader background in mental health. Also, they may find that they know more than they think about mental health issues as they work with young, drug-abusing clients.

Life skills education may be incorporated in regular Seven Challenges group work, or can be taught separately in life skills lessons or classes. Either way, connections are made to The Seven Challenges Process so that young people understand our holistic approaches and why they are being taught these various life skills.

Although planning and leading individual and group sessions require creative initiative, counselors do not have to keep re-inventing the wheel. A collection of activities for use in The Seven Challenges Program has been compiled in the book *The Seven Challenges Activities* and is provided to offer a menu of options. There are numerous other books available in bookstores about life skills education or group activities that can be integrated into work with The Seven Challenges.

THE MAD RUSH
FOR
ABSTINENCE

PRESSURE FOR IMMEDIATE ABSTINENCE

Aware of the harm and potential harm from drugs, most adults who work with drug abusing and drug dependent teens would like to see these young people become abstinent immediately. They want to protect them. Their well-meaning motives are reinforced by *enormous, external pressure for immediate abstinence*: Parents, schools, the courts and correctional settings want drug-free children…and they want them now! Individuals who work in the treatment field feel this pressure to deliver the desired outcome: drug-free children quickly. The result of this pressure has been *a mad rush for abstinence* in which drug treatment counselors try to convince young people to quit, or cajole them, or even coerce them into quitting. In this context, counselors tend to focus narrowly upon the harmfulness of drugs – and pound away on this topic. They cut off or dismiss discussion about drug benefits, and persist with pressure for immediate decisions to quit.

Mainstream approaches of this sort have not been proven to be effective.[9] Drug problems do not start overnight, nor can they be remedied overnight. Often drug problems are the culmination of a lifetime of other problems. Furthermore, counselors must consider readiness to change and the building blocks to success.

Counselors should not assume that youth, many of whom are dragged into treatment by their collars, are ready to tell the truth and make instant changes in their lives.

They should not assume that underlying and co-occurring problems associated with drug use are quickly and easily overcome.

They should not assume that youth in drug treatment possess all the life skills and abilities that would enable them to successfully care for themselves or meet their needs without drugs.

They should not assume that youth have enough self-confidence to believe that they could succeed in quitting drugs, even if they wanted to quit.

No matter how much they may want quick fixes to the drug problem, counselors have to be patient enough to find methods that are effective and start where young people are at, not where they wish they might be.

The mad rush for abstinence that has typified drug treatment for adolescence has generally elicited either of four negative response patterns, all described below, all beginning with the letter F. Youth who follow these patterns can be categorized as *Fakers, Flee-ers, Fighters* or *Followers*. These response patterns offer a likely explanation for the poor outcomes and low retention rates that have historically characterized drug counseling for adolescents.

FAKERS

Fakers tell adults what they want to hear. They readily say they will quit using drugs. They will go through all the motions of pretending to learn how to be drug free. They know that this is the quickest way to get out of drug treatment. In the mad rush for abstinence, adults teach these young people how to be drug free *before* they have even decided they want to be drug free. The youth fake it. They *say* they will quit, but clandestinely keep using. If they are in residential or correctional settings, they *say* they will quit, accept counseling as if they were serious about it, but resume using drugs quickly, as soon as an opportunity presents itself. Later they like to boast that they told the adults "what they wanted to hear." It is easy to get these young people to say they intend to quit. The much bigger challenge is to get them to say what they really think and feel, which usually is that they have no intention whatsoever of really quitting.

FLEE-ERS (THOSE WHO FLEE)

No one wants to be controlled by others. This is especially true of adolescents who, as part of a developmental process, are striving to form their own independent identities. Healthy adolescents do not want to be told what to think or do. They are likely to resist adults who they perceive as trying to dictate behavior and control them.

Many of those who flee treatment simply say, "You can't make me" and leave — or try to leave. These are the youth who don't return to outpatient settings or try to run away from residential placements.

Others flee from the mad rush for abstinence because of fear. They hear that they must give up drugs, but feel ill prepared to do so. They fear their life would be worse without drugs (for example, they would be in a lot of emotional pain). Some fear that they would fail if they really tried to quit, so they flee from drug counseling to avoid a failure experience.

The large numbers of individuals who flee from counseling account for the low retention rate of adolescents in drug treatment. Even among those who do not drop out, many others flee psychologically. They are physically present, but psychologically absent.

FIGHTERS

The mad rush for abstinence tends to result in contentious and argumentative sessions. It generates resistance. Counselors talk about the dangers of drugs, and youth resist — either openly or passively. The tone is oppositional; the outcome of the counseling effort is predictable.

"Fighters" resist adults whom they see as trying to dictate or control their behavior. Some fighters engage in open, straightforward resistance during individual or group sessions. They say it is all "stupid" or "a waste of time." Seeking attention and power, many others waste countless hours of counseling time with oblique resistance as they engage in the games of "Try to convince me that drugs are dangerous (or that I have a problem)," or "Try to make me quit." These are passive- aggressive games that frustrate adults (pages 127-135).

In outpatient settings, fighters generally waste time through either passive-aggressive or open resistance, or are asked to leave. In residential settings, they usually fight adult influence for a while with open or passive resistance, but eventually realize they cannot beat the adults who run the system. At this point, most become fakers in order to gain their release.

FOLLOWERS

Followers are the adolescents who respond positively to well meaning and caring adults who are in a mad rush for abstinence. They are swayed to wanting to quit drugs, and make a sincere commitment to change. Unfortunately, when adults are in a mad rush, they pay insufficient attention to laying a solid groundwork for success — including the intensive focus needed to remediate underlying and co-occurring problems. Followers will try hard to quit, but generally fail because of insufficient preparation. For them, the outcome is another failure experience – something many of them have already experienced all too often.

It is not surprising that outcomes have been so disappointing in adolescent drug treatment, and the dropout rates have been so high. With the mad rush for abstinence, young people either "fake it" (telling adults "what they want to hear"), fight (defy or resist), or flee from adults. Or as followers, they fail because they have been inadequately prepared for success.

SLOWING DOWN THE CHANGE PROCESS: THE LONG ROAD TO SUCCESS

The mad rush for abstinence runs counter to common sense and to so much of what we know about human nature, adolescent development, the change process, and the principles of good counseling. We should not attempt to teach people how to be drug free before they have *decided* they want to be drug free. This is straightforward common sense: We don't put the carriage before the horse. People should make decisions about their behavior *after* they have thought through the issues, not beforehand. The common sense idea of slowing the rush for abstinence is also supported and amplified by research findings about the stages of change in overcoming behavioral problems: There are preparatory stages that precede willingness, capability, and commitment to take successful action.

Furthermore, we know enough about human development to know that we should not try to control the behavior of adolescent clients. No one wants to be controlled, and this is especially true of adolescents who are forming their own independent identities.

The Seven Challenges Program avoids the mad rush for abstinence. It takes corrective action to ensure better outcomes in adolescent drug counseling. We initiate the change process slowly: building a relationship, starting where youth are "at," and helping them think things through for themselves. We help them progress through the many stages of change. With our assistance, they identify their own problems for themselves, determine it is in their own best interest to change, learn how to make changes, and begin to believe that they can be successful in making changes. Then they can make their own decisions, and we can support them as they successfully implement the desired changes.

It should be noted that this is entirely consistent with the traditional role of the counselor, as well as with research findings about positive outcomes in counseling. The traditional counseling role is not to control behavior or tell people how to behave. Doing so is condescending, takes away personal power, and is likely to increase resistance. Instead, drug counselors should perform the traditional role of the profession, which is to help clients think things through for themselves, know their options, expand their options, establish their own goals, and attain success in their own quest for wellness.[10]

There is considerable evidence, as well, that effective counseling with positive outcomes depends to a large extent upon a positive client/counselor relationship, in which the client feels that the counselor listens, understands, and empathizes with his or her story.[11] This cannot occur in the context of an argumentative, contentious relationship in which the counselor tries to control the behavior of the client. We need to engage youth in the counseling process, not antagonize them and turn them off.

THE STAGES OF CHANGE

Common sense and what we know about adolescent development are two good reasons to stop the mad rush to get teens to commit to immediate abstinence. Another strong argument against the mad rush can be found in a body of research, mentioned earlier, about the way people change. Prochaska et al.[12] studied the change process by first looking at the way people overcome tobacco addiction. Later they studied how people overcome the abuse of other drugs, as well as how they alter a variety of health-compromising behaviors.

They found that people basically go through six stages of change: pre-contemplation, contemplation, preparation, action, maintenance, and termination. They go through these stages whether they change with the assistance of a self-help group, such as AA; in treatment, with professionals; or on their own, without assistance.

It is important to look at these stages because the researchers also recognized that the choice of intervention strategies should be keyed to the stage of change. As you will see, treatment professionals working with adolescents have tended to gloss over the early stages of change, and poorly matched the treatment methods to the stage of the individuals.

In the *pre-contemplation* stage, an individual does not recognize the existence of a problem, or is unwilling to honestly acknowledge it. In the *contemplation* stage, an individual is beginning to think that maybe there is a problem. For example, an adolescent with a drug problem may think: "Well, my grades have fallen in school.

I'm getting in trouble. I said I would never smoke marijuana on school days, but now I do. I said I would never use cocaine, and now I'm using it. I better think about this. Something does seem to be wrong." Also, a person in the contemplation stage may be quite aware of the problem, but still contemplating – trying to decide – whether or not to do something about it: "I know I have a problem, but I'm not sure I want to change, or that I could change."

People in the *preparation* stage are getting ready and making plans for a substantial change that they intend to make within a month. They acknowledge that they have a problem, and may even take certain preliminary actions. For example, a person with a drinking problem may experiment with short-term abstinence (sobriety sampling) to see how it goes. In this stage of change, people are getting ready to take strong, decisive action.

Individuals enter the *action* stage when they take the type of significant behavioral action that experts say needs to be taken in order to overcome the particular problem. For example, this occurs when someone with a tobacco addiction actually quits smoking, or begins systematically reducing his or her use until becoming tobacco-free.

After six months of success in the action stage, individuals enter the maintenance stage of change. This is when previous progress is consolidated and incorporated as part of a changed lifestyle. During this stage, individuals must exercise caution to avoid letting down their guard, which could result in relapse.

The final stage of change is *termination* when the problem has been completely overcome. People in this stage can be exposed to "high-risk situations" without reverting to the problem behavior. With alcohol and other drug (AOD) problems, a person who is abstaining would feel no temptation to drink or use drugs under any circumstance. Some people with certain problems are always at risk. For example, there are people who can never drink again and must always remain vigilant, or "in recovery." In other words, termination does not necessarily apply to all people with all problems. Nonetheless, many people have had problems in their lives that they have totally overcome.

It should be noted that people do not always move in one direction in the change process. There may be advances and setbacks from one stage to another as people find their way through the change process. For example, people may contemplate about having a problem, decide they don't, and move back to pre-contemplation. People may be in the action stage, try to make a change, suffer a setback, and move back to earlier stages – either preparation, contemplation or even pre-contemplation. Then they can resume their efforts at changing, but from an earlier stage.

For optimal outcomes in treatment, clinical interventions should be matched to the stage of change. Generally speaking, there is an especially important dividing line that distinguishes between appropriate interventions for the action stage, and those that follow, from appropriate interventions in the three earlier stages of change. In the action stage and those that follow, individuals benefit most from *behavioral interven-*

tions; that is, interventions that are designed to teach behavior. For example, people who have decided to quit smoking tobacco would be taught how to quit and maintain abstinence. They would learn a variety of behaviors such as how to systematically reduce their smoking until they quit or how to quit "cold turkey." With this latter approach, they would learn to establish a quit day, what to do on the day they quit, and how to resist urges to smoke. With other drug problems, behavioral interventions in the action stage would be designed either to help individuals maintain abstinence and avoid relapse, or to moderate and control their use of substances. They would develop a relapse prevention plan, learn how to initiate and maintain a healthy lifestyle, and strive to overcome psychological and other problems that motivated their drug use.

In the three stages that precede the action stage (pre-contemplation, contemplation, and preparation), individuals have not yet committed to making changes. They are either unaware of problems, thinking about problems, or perhaps in the process of making decisions about future action. The type of interventions that are most appropriate with individuals in these stages could generally be classified as *consciousness-raising*. Such interventions help people gain awareness and insight, and ultimately decide to change. Individuals may need help thinking through their situation, trying to determine whether they have a problem. If they deem they do have one, then they would consider what they might be able to do about it, whether for example, they feel they are capable of making the changes, and whether the particular behavior changes would make their life better and be worth the effort.

People are not ready for the action stage until they have decided a change is needed and desirable, understood what is necessary to make the change, prepared themselves to change, and committed themselves to making the change. Then, it is time to learn the new behavior.

ABSTINENCE BASED? DISEASE MODEL? HARM REDUCTION?

There are numerous theoretical and political controversies that surround the field of substance abuse treatment for adolescents. The Seven Challenges Program maintains its clinical focus, without engaging in some of the hot political battles.

The Seven Challenges has been practiced successfully by people who think in terms of the disease model, and those who do not. It has been used by people who call themselves abstinence-based, by those who say they practice harm reduction, and by others.

Whether counselors think in terms of disease or not, they still have to help young people harness all of their power and abilities to make good decisions. Whether the goal of those who run a program is stated as abstinence or harm reduction, young people still need to learn to make wise decisions. This is universally agreed upon as important. Thus, The Seven Challenges Program supports young people in making good decisions, regardless of the political or theoretical position of practitioners.

INSISTING UPON ABSTINENCE

We all wish that young people in treatment would immediately quit using drugs. A small percentage of those who come to our attention *really* want to quit. Another small percentage will quit on our insistence. Perhaps some can be swayed by a hard line. The problem, however, is that most young people are far from ready to succeed with abstinence. It is too simplistic to dismiss this un-readiness as mere rebellion or defiance, although these can be factors. There are other psychologically significant impediments to change that must be addressed when working with youth. Youth may be in earlier stages of change because:

- They may not recognize that they have a problem, perhaps because they live in families or communities where drug use is almost universal, or because they do not understand the nature of drug abuse, or because of psychological reasons, unique to themselves.

- They may see a problem, but not be aware of any way to resolve it.

- They may see a problem and a way to resolve it, but feel overwhelmed by the thought of what their lives would be like if they did not have drugs as a crutch. (Here are a few examples: Young clients may be clinically *depressed*, perhaps even suicidal, and have so much distress that they do not feel they could cope without drugs; young clients may experience so much *anxiety* in their daily lives that they do not feel they could make it through the day without drugs; young clients may *suffer such pain* from abuse, or other trauma, that they do not feel they could cope with these feelings without drugs.) They feel hopeless about their lives getting better.

- They may want to make changes, but feel immobilized by fear of failure. They don't believe they could succeed with abstinence. Some of them have already had numerous failure experiences and want to prevent another one. They are so afraid of failing that they do not want to take the risk of trying.

- Even if youth know they have a problem, know what can be done about it, want to do something about it, and feel they would be successful in changing, they still may lack the life skills or be plagued by psychological problems that would prevent them from succeeding.

So in working with youth with substance abuse problems, we have a lot of initial groundwork to lay in order to get them to the point where they will be ready, willing, and able to stop abusing drugs.

The Seven Challenges Manual   ©2004 Robert Schwebel, Ph.D.

UNDERSTANDING THE SEVEN CHALLENGES

THE SEVEN CHALLENGES PROCESS

As you will see below, The Seven Challenges process is a common sense, decision-making approach to working with drug issues. It gives young people an opportunity to scrutinize the benefits and harm from their drug use, and make their own decisions. However, first the emphasis is on creating an open and trusting atmosphere in which young people feel safe to talk honestly about themselves and their lives (Challenge One.) This allows for full disclosure and consideration of all information. Then young people have a chance to look at the benefits of drug use (Challenge Two) and compare them to the costs (Challenge Three) and future costs (Challenge Five). They also can put their drug use and other behavior into the context of all of their experiences (Challenge Four) to feel strong and empowered about moving forward. Finally they make decisions about their drug use and other behaviors (Challenge Six), and then implement and evaluate their efforts to change (Challenge Seven).

Below is a list of The Seven Challenges followed by a more detailed discussion of each challenge, one at a time. Counselors implementing the program must fully understand this process.

1. We decided to open up and talk honestly about ourselves and about alcohol and other drugs.

2. We looked at what we liked about alcohol and other drugs and why we were using them.

3. We looked at our use of alcohol and other drugs to see if it had caused harm, or could cause harm.

4. We looked at our responsibility and the responsibility of others for our problems.

5. We thought about where we seemed to be headed, where we wanted to go, and what we wanted to accomplish.

6. We made thoughtful decisions about our lives and about our use of alcohol and other drugs.

7. We followed through on our decisions about our lives and drug use. If we saw problems, we went back to earlier challenges and mastered them.

© 1995 Robert Schwebel

You will see that some of the following section repeats and reinforces previous discussion about the change process. However, now you will see how this discussion relates specifically to each of the challenges.

CHALLENGE ONE

We decided to open up and talk honestly about ourselves and about alcohol and other drugs.

It is important to create an open and safe climate in a counseling program in which honest discussion can take place. We should bear in mind that most young people do not come to drug treatment of their own free will. Many do not even think that they have problems. Many of them mistrust adults. They expect that drug counselors will *try to convince them or make them quit* using drugs. They are certain that drug counselors are working with only one purpose in mind – which is to make them quit. They may have been previously exposed to aggressive and combative drug treatment, or been around adults who simply moralized about their "bad behavior." The mad rush for abstinence has done nothing but reinforce this expectation in youth. We need to slow things down and help young people warm up to the process. We do not want young people to think that we are trying to talk them into something, enforce our will, or *make* them quit using drugs. We want to help them make their own wise choices. This is the appropriate role for counselors.

Most youth with drug problems have a history of lying. But they also are used to being around adults with whom, when they told the truth, they only got in more trouble. We have to create a safe climate for them. Unless an effort is made to undo the negative expectations about drug counseling (that adults want to control their behavior and *make* them quit using drugs), young clients will be inclined to tell lies, mislead adults, and put up resistance. In Challenge One, negative expectations must be overcome so that counselors and clients can begin to build a positive and trusting relationship. This allows young people to begin to look honestly at themselves — including at the importance of avoiding denial — and to talk openly with others. Without taking an honest look at oneself and one's life, it is impossible to make informed decisions.

When clients open up and talk honestly, they are making themselves vulnerable. Therefore, counselors must also go to great lengths to protect their emotional and physical safety.

Key concepts of Challenge One: Trust, safety, and relationships.

CHALLENGE TWO

We looked at what we liked about alcohol and other drugs and why we were using them.

In Challenge Two, young people have an opportunity to think about and discern which needs they are satisfying or attempting to satisfy through their drug use. That is, they are looking at the perceived benefits of drugs. They get help in moving from a general and global sense of what they like about drugs (for example: they feel good) to a more detailed and clear understanding of the benefits (for example: they feel good because they make me feel more relaxed; they feel good because they make me forget my worries; they feel good because they take away my boredom, etc.). In working through this challenge, young people get an idea of what needs they meet from using drugs. They find, for example, that they use drugs to relax, to forget problems, to enjoy social situations, to moderate their anger, to quell boredom and have fun, for diversion, and for excitement. Sometimes they discover that they use different drugs at different times for different reasons. In order for counselors to fully understand the extent of drug use, make a good assessment, and understand clients (and for a number of other reasons discussed later in this manual), they must give young people an opportunity to think and talk freely about what they like about drugs (pages 48-50). Providing this opportunity is part of The Seven Challenges' Counseling Approaches. Many counselors find it difficult to really stick with this because they worry about appearing to enable drug use or approve of it. They want to argue about the harmful effects of drugs and the need to quit.

Challenge Two provides a window to understanding the problems that co-occur with substance abuse, such as anxiety, depression, oppositional-defiant behavior, post-traumatic stress, and others. It also sheds light on youth deficiencies in various life skills.

Key concepts of Challenge Two: Drug benefits, self-understanding, meeting needs, and satisfying desires.

CHALLENGE THREE

We looked at our use of alcohol and other drugs to see if it had caused harm, or could cause harm.

In making health decisions about drugs, it is important to consider the harm from their use – and the *potential harm*. Potential harm is harm that could occur as a result of the current behavior, but has not yet happened. For example, under the influence of drugs, there is the risk of causing an auto wreck, getting involved in an unwanted pregnancy, or transmitting or catching a sexually transmitted disease. There is also the risk of drug overdose. For some individuals, there is increased risk of engaging in criminal activity.

In evaluating harm from drug use, young people tend to think in terms of extremes: addiction and dependence. In their minds, only addicted individuals have drug problems. Addiction is discussed in this challenge. Also, drug abuse is discussed, including the idea that even a single incident of drug use can lead to serious negative consequences. This is especially a problem with adolescents with whom drug use can be opportunistic and episodic.[13] That is, they use drugs whenever they are available. But when they are available, they use *all that is available*. This can result in bingeing and serious consequences. Another consideration with adolescents is what happens to them when they use drugs over and over again to deal with life. This may feel good on the short run, but such use of drugs deprives them of an opportunity to learn the social, personal, educational, and psychological skills they need to be learning at this stage of their lives. This avoidance keeps them from maturing. Finally, Challenge Three helps young people understand that harm from drugs is not limited to harm to oneself. It generally leads to harm to one's family, other individuals, and the community.

Typically, traditional drug treatment for adolescents has narrowly focused on adults talking at great length about the harm and dangers from drugs. They devote considerable effort to trying to convince young people that drugs are dangerous, and that they should quit using them. This argumentative approach has generally led to defensiveness and resistance. Then, when clients defend their drug use, they are told that they are "in denial." Counseling sessions become battles. Often they degenerate into the game of "You haven't convinced me drugs are dangerous"; or "You haven't convinced me to quit." One of the crucial counseling skills in The Seven Challenges is how to address the topic of harm from drugs, without arousing or provoking defensiveness. We have to be clever about this. This cleverness must extend to our work in drug education, as well, which is also part of Challenge Three. (How to approach the harm from drug use without promoting defensiveness will be discussed in more detail later in this manual, on pages 52-57.)

Key concepts of Challenge Three: Harm, negative consequences, abuse and dependence.

CHALLENGE FOUR

We looked at our responsibility and the responsibility of others for our problems.

Challenge Four is designed to help young people understand themselves in the context of their life experiences. They can see the influence – both positive and negative – of their family, other people around them, and their circumstances. They can see the opportunities and limitations they have experienced. Within this context, they can understand how they have come to behave in the ways that they do.

By putting personal problems in perspective, Challenge Four helps young people validate themselves. Validation allows them to recognize and accept their own flaws, weaknesses, and mistakes because they understand where they came from. (Teaching young people how to validate their experiences is a Seven Challenges counseling skill that will be discussed in more detail later, on pages 58-60.)

Validation is important because youth who abuse drugs often inflict a great deal of harm on themselves, their families, and their communities. *Many youth internalize responsibility and blame themselves, and themselves alone, for all their problems and wrongdoing.* It is not uncommon that they feel enormous shame about their behavior — such shame that they cannot admit to problems and therefore cannot move forward in correcting them. They are paralyzed. However, many of these young people have themselves been victimized or traumatized. Many have been physically or sexually abused, or witnessed violence... sometimes even in their own homes. Often they use alcohol or other drugs to cope with the pain and emotional trauma of such experiences.[14] Young people also use drugs to deal with stressful and painful situations and to self medicate against various negative emotions such as anxiety, sadness, and loneliness.[15] They may never have learned other, healthier ways to cope.

Validation counteracts the disabling affects of self-blame, shame and guilt. It empowers people to take responsibility for their behavior, to feel strong, and to make important changes in their lives. It is a paradox: To the extent that individuals can see how their situation and other people have contributed to their problems, they are better able to accept their own share of the responsibility. In contrast, when they blame themselves for everything, they generally feel shame and overwhelming power-lessness.

Some drug abusing youth go to the opposite extreme from self-blame. They justify their problem behavior and cover up their own responsibility by shifting all the blame and responsibility to others. This results, sometimes, from the psychological defense mechanism of projection. Youth feel such overwhelming personal shame that they must project it onto others. Also, putting all blame on others can be a form of expressing intense and often legitimate anger in response to how these young people have been treated. Regardless of cause, blaming others and blaming "the world" for everything keeps them from seeing their own share of the responsibility, and keeps them from seeing what they can do to make things better. Blinded by rage, these young people need to learn to be self-critical so they can make changes and move forward.

Challenge Four is designed to counteract these two types of over-simplistic thinking:

- "I am to blame for all my problems." (People who think this way tend to be depressed.)

- "Others are to blame for all my problems." (People who think this way tend to be angry.)

In this challenge, young people learn to conduct fair and even-handed constructive criticism. They see how others have harmed them. They also see what they are doing wrong and need to change.

Key concepts of Challenge Four: Responsibility; validation; constructive criticism.

CHALLENGE FIVE

We thought about where we seemed to be headed, where we wanted to go, and what we wanted to accomplish.

This challenge helps young people develop a future orientation: to consider where they are headed, where they would like to go, and how their current choices and drug use may affect their future. It has two different aspects. One the one hand, this challenge explores the potential harm from continued drug use and from continuing along the existing trajectory. On the one hand, this challenge is visionary, giving clients an opportunity to imagine and consider what they want for themselves in the future.

Whereas Challenge Three is about current harm from drug use, Challenge Five incorporates the issue of long-term harm. In the early stages of drug use, harm may be minimal. Also, young children are protected from some of the immediate conse-quences because their parents feed and shelter them. Later, however, the harm becomes much more obvious. Young people who spend their adolescent years getting high instead of going to school and learning various life skills will not be prepared for adulthood. Challenge Five helps young people look ahead and anticipate their future. They have an opportunity to think about where they are headed and where they want to go. Often they discover a discrepancy between the two. This challenge brings the future to bear upon current appraisals of the cost and benefits of drug use. Key questions include these: If you keep going the way you are headed, where will you end? Where do you want to be? If you keep using drugs, what will happen? What are your values? What is important to you? What do you want to make of yourself?

During the adolescent developmental stage, young people are supposed to be preparing for their future as young adults. This challenge taps that developmental urge.

In this challenge, young people get to think about their connections to other people – and where they fit with friends, family, their community, and their society. They get to think about the big picture beyond their momentary and material needs. For those who are spiritually oriented, this is a time to think about their beliefs and spiritual values.

Another important aspect of Challenge Five is inspiring young people to get in touch with their dreams and goals – and generating optimism and hope about the future. For some people, Challenge Five is about reestablishing hope that life can be better. People do not make changes in their lives unless they think that their lives will be better as a result of the changes.

Key concepts of Challenge Five: Future, future orientation, values, goals, dreams, hope and optimism.

CHALLENGE SIX

We made thoughtful decisions about our lives and about our use of alcohol and other drugs.

Challenge Six is consistent with the basic counseling goal of helping people make their own choices. In this challenge, young people make decisions about changes they want to make in all aspects of their lives, including with regard to their drug use. The Seven Challenges Program does not prescribe the decision. A selling point to young people is that this program is the only drug treatment program for adolescents that does *not* tell them how to live their lives. It does not say that young people must decide to be drug free. Rather, young people are asked to make their own wise decisions about their lives and their drug use. This is also consistent with what we know about the developmental tasks of adolescence: Young people need to figure out their own identity and start making their own decisions. (Counselors who use The Seven Challenges and identify themselves as "abstinence-based" would still believe that abstinence is indicated. However, they would be unwise to set themselves up for rebellion, for example, by making demands which will increase the likelihood that young clients might say: "I won't be drug free because you are telling me that I *must* be drug free." Also, abstinence-based counselors realize that ultimately young people cannot be controlled. We have to set up the best possible conditions for them to make the best possible decisions.)

Although The Seven Challenges does not state that young people must be drug free, there are strong factors built into the program to protect against foolish decisions. First, by the time decision-making takes place, young people have had a chance to fully consider the harm, potential harm, and future harm that could occur from drug abuse. Also, they have learned and strengthened skills that increase their capability of meeting their needs without drugs. If they have truly worked the program, it is highly unlikely that drug abusing youth would think it wise to continue using drugs. Furthermore, there is additional protection. Challenge Seven is the follow up. If drug-abusing young people naively decide that they can keep using drugs, they will soon discover the folly of this decision as they continue with Challenge Seven.

The holistic approach of the Seven Challenges Program is evident in Challenge Six because emphasis is placed on the importance of making changes both with regard to drug problems and to co-occurring problems. Youth will have to make parallel decisions. Seven Challenges sessions and published materials make it clear that drug decisions cannot be made independently of decisions about lifestyle changes (adopting new attitudes, solving certain problems, learning new life skills, and learning problem solving and coping skills). For example: If individuals choose to quit using drugs, they usually have to find new ways to have fun; drop some old friends and make some new ones; find new ways to cope with stress; find new ways to deal with personal problems; and find new ways to manage their emotions, such as anger. In other words, the needs they were formerly trying to satisfy by using drugs will now have to be met in different ways. Also, in terms of friends, they will have to establish a new social network.

The essential objective in Challenge Six is helping clients make fully informed, internally motivated, and committed decisions to change. Counselors try to prevent young people from rushing to commit to something before they fully understand the nature and extent of the commitment. In making decisions about *drugs*, clients are urged in this Challenge to slow down and think carefully – to deliberate. Before committing to certain behavior, such as the decision to be drug free, it is important that a foundation is laid for success. It is important that people understand what they are giving up, how hard it may be to successfully implement this decision, and that they must have motivation and skills that match the challenge. The idea is to prepare people for success when they make such decisions, and to avoid the pitfall of deciding to make changes and then experiencing failure.

By placing confidence in young people about their own decision-making skills and by supporting them as they make changes, The Seven Challenges Program promotes a sense of self-confidence and increased self worth in young people.

Key Concepts of Challenge Six: Drug decisions and lifestyle decisions; preparing for decisions, committing to them, and steps toward behavioral implementation; the holistic approach.

CHALLENGE SEVEN

We followed through on our decisions about our lives and drug use. If we saw problems, we went back to earlier challenges and mastered them.

Challenge Seven is about following through on decisions. It is about behavioral change. Young people follow through on decisions they made in terms of lifestyle changes: attitudes they want to change; life skills they want to master; problem situations they want to correct. They also follow through on their drug decisions with state of the art relapse prevention. As young people follow through on their own decisions, they evaluate their progress. They also learn to balance high expectations with an understanding that mistakes and setbacks are part of the process. Young people learn from their experiences, including the problems and setbacks. They are encouraged to get support and feedback from others. If possible, they are connected to self-help and support groups in the community.

Key Concepts of Challenge Seven: Follow through with behavior change; learning from experience; realistic expectations; support; relapse prevention; evaluation of progress.

GOING THROUGH THE SEVEN CHALLENGES

Logically, it would seem that young people would move through The Seven Challenges in a linear way, from Challenge One to Two, to Three, etc., on to Seven. In reality, however, they work on different challenges simultaneously, or at any point in their work. Clearly they must begin to lay groundwork for their efforts by opening up and talking honestly. This is Challenge One. But as they continue in the program, there will be new obstacles to openness and honesty, and work on Challenge One must be ongoing. It also makes sense to start by allowing a free discussion of drug benefits (Challenge Two). This shows young people that their counselors are serious about creating an open and honest atmosphere: There is even freedom to talk about what they *like* about drugs. This discussion begins early, but later in the process young people may gain additional awareness of other needs they have been satisfying, or trying to satisfy, by using drugs. Often, clients will be working on several challenges at once. For example: They may be considering what they like about drugs (Challenge Two) and the harm from drugs (Challenge Three) and the future harm (Challenge Five) on the same day — in a single exercise that calls for opening up with others (Challenge One). Or, while making decisions about their future use of drugs (Challenge Six), young people may become aware of harm (Challenge Three), future harm (Challenge Five) or benefits (Challenge Two). It could be said that, at times, they may be bouncing around from challenge to challenge in their work.

There is one aspect of the program, however, that gives continuity to the progression through the challenges. That is, young people work on their journals one at a time. They must successfully complete the first journal before moving on to the second. They must successfully complete the second before moving on to the third, and so on.

Thus, the written work provides a strong measure of grounding and continuity as youth progress in The Seven Challenges Program.

THE SEVEN CHALLENGES COUNSELING APPROACHES

SUBSTANCE ABUSE COUNSELING AS A SPECIALTY FIELD

Substance abuse counseling is considered a specialty within the field of counseling and psychotherapy. As such, state of the art skills are not something that anyone should expect to master without extensive training and experience. Nevertheless, counselors and other youth workers without specialty training are often asked to work with young people with drug problems. They need to seek additional knowledge and training. We need to help them acquire the requisite skills. There are many ways that adults can help young people with drug problems through conversation and counseling. This section of the handbook outlines key approaches to working with young people that are basic to The Seven Challenges. Some are harder to apply and master than others. Here are some ideas that should prove helpful in working with adolescents with AOD problems.

KEY CONSIDERATIONS IN ADOLESCENT DRUG COUNSELING

The Seven Challenges Counseling Approaches are based on the recognition of several key factors:

- Adolescents have certain developmental tasks that include forming their own individual identity, learning mature logical thinking, and preparing for adulthood. They do not take kindly to being told what to do, or to efforts aimed at controlling them.

- Many, if not most, young people who abuse or are dependent upon drugs have co-occurring problems such as depression and anxiety problems, and deficits in social and personal life skills. They may be experiencing intense feelings of shame, anger, anxiety, and hopelessness.

- Many young people with drug problems have been traumatized by physical or sexual abuse, or by being witnesses to violence, sometimes in their own families.

- The vast majority of young people do not come to drug counseling of their own free will.

- Because the vast majority of adolescents do not seek treatment themselves, most are in the earlier stages of the change process. Many do not think they have a drug problem, or would be unwilling to honestly admit to one. Others may have some concerns about drug use but are far from ready to committing to do something about making changes.

- Many mistrust adults and have the habit of lying.

- Most expect that adult AOD counselors have only one purpose – to make them quit using drugs; either by talking them into it, or by coercing them. They have misperceptions about the role of the counselor and mistrust of counselors.

This section of the manual is about the basic clinical approaches of The Seven Challenges Program. Certain clinical skills and principles are essential for optimal success with the program. Each challenge has clinical skills and principles closely associated with it that will be presented below, challenge-by-challenge.

CHALLENGE ONE CLINICAL SKILLS
UNDOING NEGATIVE EXPECTATIONS, CREATING A CLIMATE OF HONESTY, ESTABLISHING TRUST, AND REDEFINING SUCCESS

UNDOING NEGATIVE EXPECTATIONS

Many if not most youth have a negative impression of drug counseling. They believe it will be a combative event in which adults try to make them quit, perhaps by exaggerating the dangers of drugs, perhaps by hammering away about the harm, and perhaps by attempts at coercion. They expect that adults will not be especially interested in their perspective (how they see things) and probably will not tolerate discussion of what they really like about drugs. Unless counselors proactively address this issue, youth will be primed to resist or be dishonest with them. One of the most important clinical principles in working with The Seven Challenges Program is that *counselors must undo the negative expectations that youth have about them and their role.*

INTRODUCING OURSELVES TO YOUTH

The way in which counselors introduce themselves and The Seven Challenges Program can be a positive first step toward undoing negative expectations that young people have about drug counseling. In their own personal introduction, counselors can give their name and title, and perhaps surprise a young person with a statement of this sort:

"Even though I lead the drug group here, it's really not as bad as it sounds. I won't exaggerate the dangers of drugs. I'm not going to hammer away about the harm from drugs. I'm not going to try to talk you out of using drugs. When you work with me, you don't have to say you're going to quit using drugs to be successful. My job is to help you think things through for yourself. You are old enough now to make your own choices about your life and the use of alcohol and other drugs. No one can or should follow you around and tell you what to do. It is a time in life when you have to think for yourself. My job is to support you in that. I assure you I will not try to talk you into anything."

In short: "I'm not here to make you quit using drugs. My job is to help you think things through for yourself. If you're already doing this, you'll especially like the support you'll be getting from me."

The sort of personal introduction described above is consistent with the *traditional role of a counselor.* That role has not been to dictate or control the behavior of clients. Rather the counselor role is to help people with self-understanding and decision-making and, when possible, to expand their options. We expand options by helping clients become aware of existing options they may not have noticed, and by teaching new skills. We surely know and understand the harm caused by young people using drugs, and may believe that quitting would be in the best interest of virtually all the youth we encounter. Nevertheless, it is still not our job to try to talk them into anything. Doing so would be contrary to our role and to what is effective, and to what we know about supporting adolescent development.

INTRODUCING THE PROGRAM

Explaining how The Seven Challenges Program works – emphasizing that it is respectful and does not dictate behavior — can also help undo the negative expectations about drug treatment. Specific help in how to introduce the program is provided later in this manual, in the section on implementation on page 71.

INCREASING TRUST

For a variety of reasons, many youth do not feel safe talking openly and honestly with adults. We need to encourage honesty. By the same token, we need to create a safe environment (see pages 81-83 on rules), and proactively address obstacles to trust and honesty – both within our clients and in our relationships with them. The critical questions to ask clients are: What do we need to do to make you feel safe? What do you need to do to open up and talk honestly?

REDEFINE SUCCESS IN SMALLER INCREMENTS

Most young people enter treatment far from ready to make a sincere commitment to abstinence, and far from prepared to be successful should they make such a commitment. If they believe their treatment program is based on the premise of instant abstinence, they will probably conclude, "It's not for me." They may not think that they have a problem. They may be far from ready to honestly admit to a problem. They may not believe that their life would be better if they were to quit drugs. If young people see only one treatment goal – immediate commitment to, and success with, abstinence – they will be convinced that the treatment is not suitable to their needs. The bar is set too high, with no way to get over the top. Furthermore, many of them would not see any reason to try.

So, it is important to redefine success for young people, and to think about it in smaller increments. There are many stages of change that precede the behavioral act of "quitting drugs." Young people need to see these steps and feel that they could master them and succeed. In the Seven Challenges Process, one important clinical principle is redefining success in smaller increments.

In The Seven Challenges Program we recognize and reinforce success as people move through the entire change process. Success is measured in small increments. We see success as youth move through the stages of change; from pre-contemplation to contemplation, from contemplation to preparation, from preparation to action, from action to maintenance, and from maintenance to termination. Anytime they suffer a setback in the change process, they are successful if they learn a lesson and get back on track. We see success as youth master each of the seven challenges. This is one reason why youth are given diplomas upon the completion of each journal (pages 113-114).

Below are some of the markers of success with The Seven Challenges:

- When youth who did not trust adults and lied to them now begin to have a measure of trust — and they open up and talk honestly

- When youth gain self understanding about what motivates their drug use – what needs they are satisfying by their consumption of alcohol or other drugs

- When youth begin to take a hard look at the harm from their drug use

- When youth who did not think that they had a problem with drugs, begin to see they might have a problem

- When youth who would not honestly admit (to others) that they had a problem, now begin to admit to it

- When youth solve life problems that co-occur with their drug use

- When youth learn new life skills that give them other ways to meet their needs without drugs

- When youth become aware of possibilities for change that they did not previously see

- When youth who felt they could not have a happy life without drugs begin to see they have the strength to make a good life for themselves

- When youth who felt they could not succeed in quitting, even if they wanted to quit, begin to gain confidence in their ability to be successful

- When youth make decisions to change

- When youth make preparations to change

- When youth follow through on various decisions to change

- When youth begin to have positive experiences of making small changes

- When youth learn from mistakes and setbacks as they change

There are numerous ways that young people can be successful in drug treatment. We need to redefine success so *they* can feel successful in our programs. By the same token, it is important that the *counselors, themselves,* begin to think in terms of smaller increments of success. If counselors measure their own success only in terms of their clients immediately choosing to be abstinent, they are more likely to fall into the trap of the mad rush for abstinence. This will lead them to pressure youth, and is likely to result in increased resistance and dishonesty. It will interfere with the change process. Instead, clients should be considered successful all through the process as they respond by looking at their lives, considering their options, learning new skills to increase their options, thinking through their own decisions, making decisions, and then successfully implementing them.

Appendix Two of this publication identifies specific treatment goals for work on each of the seven challenges.

CHALLENGE TWO CLINICAL SKILLS
ALLOW AND ENCOURAGE YOUNG PEOPLE TO TALK ABOUT WHAT THEY LIKE ABOUT DRUGS

TEN REASONS TO ENCOURAGE DISCUSSION OF DRUG BENEFITS

If counselors are sincere about allowing young people to talk openly and honestly about their drug use (this is Challenge One work), then it means they must be prepared to let them talk freely about what they like about drugs, which is the focus of Challenge Two. Facilitating discussion of "drug benefits" is one of the most important clinical skills in The Seven Challenges Program.

Many counselors have difficulty encouraging and allowing such free discussion. They worry that this will be seen as endorsing, encouraging, or enabling drug use, or at least as giving the appearance of tacit acceptance. They worry about youth telling "war stories" and glamorizing drugs. These concerns will be addressed below. Despite these concerns, good drug counseling with young people includes allowing them to talk freely about drug benefits.

Beware of the tendency to stop or discourage this type of discussion, or to refute benefits, or to counter with an emphasis on harm. Too often well-meaning drug counselors, trying to do their job well, fall into this trap.

There is an intuitive reaction that we should not let kids talk about what they like about drugs. However, there are at least ten good reasons why we should allow such discussion:

1. To follow the principles of good counseling. Drugs are part of a young person's reality. *In counseling we need to know our clients and show our interest in knowing them.* We need to know what they think and feel. What sort of message would we be sending if we said? : "I want to know you. I want you to talk freely about yourself and your life, except, I don't want to know about what you like about drugs." Counselors need to know their clients, including what their clients like about drugs.

2. *In counseling, we need to create a safe environment for free discussion.* If we censor or cut off discussion in one realm, we reduce the likelihood of openness and full disclosure in all of the counseling.

3. *A good assessment requires full disclosure.* It is impossible to do a good assessment of a drug problem if we do not allow free discussion. If we cut off discussion of what a client likes about drugs – and the positive feelings about drugs – we cannot find

out the full extent of the drug involvement, nor make a good assessment.

4. *It shows open mindedness to our clients.* If we were not curious about the benefits from drugs, then our clients would see us as uninformed and perhaps naïve, ignorant, and narrow minded. We want our clients to be open-minded. So, we should show them that we are open-minded. Discussing benefits helps undo client beliefs that we are unaware of the benefits, as well as their expectation that we are focused only on the harm from drugs — and on trying to make them quit. It also shows that we are interested in their point of view and want to understand them. Otherwise, they are likely to feel and perhaps say, "You don't know where I'm coming from."

5. *If counselors allow free talk about the benefits of drugs, clients will be more willing to consider, admit, and discuss the harm.* When counselors show open mindedness about drug benefits, clients are more willing to let down their guard, reduce their defensiveness, and acknowledge harm and potential harm from their drug use. They will also be more open to considering our opinions about the harm.

6. *It is important that young people and their counselors know the motivation for drug use.* This is part of full understanding of the situation. Clients and counselors have to know what needs are being satisfied by the drug use.

7. *Once counselors know why young people are using drugs, they can offer validation, and express empathy about the motivation.* For example: "I see why you have been using drugs. It has been a way to relax so you could fall asleep at night when you were tense. You didn't see any other way that you could relax and get a good night's sleep." Communicating empathy is an important process for success in counseling. (More on validation on pages 58-60.)

8. *It allows counselors to become problem-solving partners with clients.* When counselors know why young people are using drugs and see what needs are being met, they can help clients identify and learn healthier ways to meet these needs. This type of alliance puts counselors in a position from which they can redefine their role in a positive way – as a problem-solving partner: "We are not here to take away drugs. We are not here to take away something that may be the only way – or a favored way – you have to satisfy certain needs. Rather we are here as your problem-solving partners. We are here to empower you with new ways to meet your needs. We are here to give you more options." With new ways to satisfy their needs, clients will be in a better position to make their own decisions to quit using drugs, if they wish to do so.

9. *It allows youth to make realistic and informed decisions.* If clients are going to do a good job of comparing the costs and benefits of a behavior, they have to know the benefits. We can't skip that side of the equation. If they are thinking about giving up a certain behavior (using drugs), they must know what they are giving up, should they decide to quit. If they lack this understanding, their decisions will be undermined. They may intend to quit using, but not fully comprehend what this

means. For example, if they use drugs to cope with anxiety, they must realize that quitting drugs means they have given up their coping mechanism. Next time they are anxious, they will not be able to resort to drugs. They must consider: Am I prepared to give up this coping mechanism?

10. *For relapse prevention, it is important that young people know the potential cues, or "triggers," for urges to use.* When people decide to quit using drugs, they must know what stimulated their urge to use in the past in order to anticipate their potential triggers for relapse. (For example: If they used drugs to forget their pain in the past, a risk factor for relapse would be situations in which they were feeling pain.) Anticipating these triggers gives young people an opportunity to prepare to cope with potential temptations after they quit using.

WHAT ABOUT GLAMORIZATION?

Counselors are sometimes uncomfortable allowing clients to talk freely about what they like about drugs because of concern that youth will start exaggerating and glamorizing drugs by telling boisterous "war stories" that depict their experiences and exploits of over-indulgence and high risk behavior. Sometimes this occurs during group sessions. However, it is important to make a distinction between an honest look at what someone likes about drugs, and a boisterous and competitive showing-off, which is the hallmark of war stories. With The Seven Challenges counseling approach, we encourage open discussion of drug benefits, but clearly distinguish this from competitive efforts at impressing peers with exploits.

A model response to war stories would be:

"One of the goals of this group is to help you make a fair, level-headed appraisal of the benefits and harm from drugs. We don't exaggerate the dangers of drugs in this group. That would be inappropriate. By the same token, we are not here to glamorize drugs by boasting about exploits. You should feel free in here to talk about what you like about drugs and how much you have liked them. But it is not appropriate to boast about your drug experiences."

When young people start telling war stories, skilled group leaders help group members gain insight from the experience. Without being critical and passing negative judgments, a group leader could point to those who tell war stories and say:

"It does seem that one need you have been meeting through your drug use is that it has been a way to be a big shot among your friends. You have been a heavy user, and have used this to impress peers. We all want to be liked by peers. We all want approval and recognition from others. It seems that you have used your drug use for this purpose. That has been one of the benefits of your drug use. If you ever decide to quit using drugs, you will have to find new ways to be recognized and to impress your peers."

ARE YOU SAYING IT IS OK TO USE DRUGS?

Allowing young people to talk freely about what they like about drugs may be confusing to the young clients, parents, and other adults.

Parents and other adults may say: "Are you saying it is OK to use drugs?" Then they would add: "It's not OK with me. That's the wrong message to give young people." It is important to clarify this misunderstanding. When counselors allow young people to talk about what they like about drugs, they are not approving of drug use. Rather, they are trying to make sense of the behavior; trying to gain understanding and greater insight into the motivation for drug use. They are also trying to help their young clients gain this same understanding. With increased understanding, clients will be better able to make wise decisions. There is a big difference between understanding the motivation for drug use and giving approval for such use.

Young people may legitimately misunderstand counselor willingness to allow discussion of the benefits of drug use, or they may manipulatively use this freedom in a power play.

They may go to their parents and say: "My counseling group says it's OK to use drugs." This is one reason why counselors should explain the program to parents, so they are prepared to deal with this sort of misunderstanding or manipulation.

During a counseling session, youth may try to make it seem as though they have counselor approval of their drug use:

"Well, you're saying it's OK to use drugs, so why are you making a fuss about....."

This is a misconception that needs to be corrected: "We are not saying it is OK to use drugs, just as we are not trying to tell you NOT to use drugs. You have to decide for yourself. Please don't misunderstand this. We know there is something you like about drugs. We want to understand what it is. It's good for you to have self-understanding and for us to understand you better. We also know that there can be very serious negative consequences from drug use."

Assuming we know enough about the youth with whom we are working to justify the following judgment, we could add:

"Knowing you, in my opinion, it is not a good idea at all for you to be using drugs. There have been some serious consequences (or will be if you keep doing what you have been doing). But, it is not my job to convince you of anything. My job is to help you think things through for yourself so you can make your own good decisions. And thinking it through does include considering what you *like* about drugs."

CHALLENGE THREE CLINICAL SKILLS
TALKING ABOUT DRUG DANGERS AND HARM

AVOID ARGUMENTATION

There is an intuitive feeling among adults that the best way to prevent drug problems in youth – or to overcome them – is to hammer away about the harmfulness of drugs. That is, we should try to convince young people that drugs are dangerous so they will not use them in the first place (drug prevention) or stop using them if they have already begun (drug treatment).

In the mad rush for abstinence, counselors often harshly confront young people about their drug use. They persistently harp on the dangers, believing that under such a barrage they could convince youth to quit using – and get them to make a sincere commitment to change. The tone is argumentative. The reaction is usually defensive. And, the discussions are contentious.

An example would be a counselor telling young clients that marijuana is bad for their lungs; could affect their fertility; will affect their memory, concentration and grades; may lead them to unsavory friends, problems in the family, and more dangerous drugs; and could even lead to problems with the law; and on and on.

A more subtle form of the same approach is the indirect onslaught: One probing question after another is asked: How would your parents feel? What about jobs? How much do you use compared to the past? How do you pay for it? What's happened to your old friends? How are you doing in school? Do you play sports? How has it affected your performance? Do you know how to get "high on life?" What about natural highs, like hiking, climbing or bike riding? All of the questions are designed to out smart, out-argue and convince a youth that marijuana is dangerous – and agree to quit.

The problem with the *harsh confrontational* or *subtle argumentative* approaches is that they usually don't work in convincing young people to quit using drugs.

We know that knowledge of drug dangers, by itself, does not lead to abstinence. This can be seen most clearly with tobacco. Most cigarette smokers have heard about the dangers of tobacco. But they persist in smoking for any number of reasons. One reason is to meet social, psychological and emotional needs. Another is because of habit, or even addiction. Still another reason is because they feel they could not succeed in quitting. Most young people have at least some vague understanding of the dangers of most drugs. They may need further education and clarification of misunderstandings about risks and harm. But they ignore or overlook this information for many reasons: They do not feel that they have a problem, that they are abusing or drug dependent. They may be in denial. They also may be wanting or needing the benefits of drugs so much that they are reluctant to even consider the harm. Also, they may see the harm as too far in the distance to matter.

Ironically: Determined, single-minded emphasis on the dangers of drug is not a very effective way of helping young people see the harm. We know that people get defensive when they are hounded and become more resistant to change. When adults try to convince young clients that drugs are harmful or that they specifically have a problem, most of them get defensive. They see us as trying to control them or make them do something. They respond with defensiveness. The more we push, the more they defend themselves from our onslaught. When youth defend marijuana and talk of its benefits, they will then be told they are "in denial."

THE REBUTTAL CYCLE

Often the harsh confrontational and subtle argumentative approaches used with youth result in the rebuttal cycle.[16] This occurs when adults and youth lock horns in a contentious power struggle:

Adult: Marijuana is dangerous. It is bad for your lungs.

Teen: Living in Los Angeles, Houston, or Phoenix is bad for your lungs. Millions of people do it. So, what!

Adult: Marijuana is illegal.

Teen: So is speeding on the freeway. You've surely done that, haven't you?

This is a debate that goes nowhere.

The rebuttal cycle is of interest in light of the work of Miller and his colleagues[17] about ambivalence. In *Motivational Interviewing*, Miller explains that most people who abuse drugs are ambivalent. On the one hand, they feel a strong attraction to drug benefits. On the other hand, they have considerable concern about the negative consequences of their drug use. Miller discusses psychological research about ambivalence, explaining that people tend to maintain the balance. So, the more one would argue about one side of the ambivalence, the stronger would be the defense of the other side. Ironically, this would mean that counselors who argue about the harm from drugs would inadvertently be actually reinforcing clients' own thinking about the benefits of drugs. Historically, this is exactly what drug counselors have done with youth. They have dwelled on the dangers. As would be predicted from the findings about ambivalence, young clients respond by defending themselves and defending the benefits of drugs. Further research[18] has shown that people who argue one position in a discussion are actually convincing themselves more fully of their own point of view as they articulate it. So, drug counselors have historically been reinforcing and strengthening a young person's view about the benefits of drugs.

When counselors try to convince young people that drugs are dangerous and that they should quit using them, many young people seize this opportunity to play the games, "Try to make me quit" and "Try to convince me that drugs are dangerous" (pages 127-135) of this manual. These games are a waste of time, and prevent individuals from doing the work that is supposed to take place in effective drug counseling.

GIVE UP IN-THE-FACE POWER

Because we want to (a) work with development, (b) avoid the rebuttal cycle, and (c) account for what we know about ambivalence, Seven Challenges counselors give up the option of using harsh, in-the-face confrontation. Too often, this has been the only sort of power that young people have experienced – in their homes, with peers, and in their communities. They are familiar with it – even comfortable with it — and know how to defend themselves from it. Instead, Seven Challenges counselors use the power of respectful education; strong supportive relationships; finesse; and non-argumentative forms of persuasion, including loving confrontation (all of which are discussed below). This not only helps young people move through the change process, but also demonstrates and teaches respect and other ways that individuals can be powerful.

Thus, another part of The Seven Challenges Counseling Approach is learning to address the issue of harm from drugs in subtle and clever ways that do not arouse defensiveness, nor promote resistance.

CONFRONTING DENIAL IN THE SEVEN CHALLENGES: GETTING TO HARM

It is widely agreed that people with drug problems often use the psychological defense mechanism of denial to protect themselves from conscious awareness of the painful reality of the seriousness of their problems. In order to identify their own drug problems, they need to overcome denial.

Counselors typically have confronted the denial of drug abusing clients with vigorous onslaughts about the harmful effects of drugs, which we now know tends to harden an opposing position and reinforce defenses. Therefore this tactic is not used in The Seven Challenges Program. So, how then can we reach young people to help them break through their denial to see that drugs have harmed them?

Below are some of the creative approaches that Seven Challenges counselors use to get young people to confront their denial, or unawareness, or difficulty in recognizing or admitting that their drug use is problematic. Special care is taken not to back youth into corners.

1. *We use readings in The Seven Challenges* book that deal with relevant issues. One particularly good one is "Lying to Ourselves" on page six. This reading reframes denial as lying to oneself, and challenges readers to ask themselves certain questions that, depending upon the response, might be indicative of denial.

2. *We use journal exercises* to deal with issues related to honesty to oneself and honesty in general. A particularly good exercise is on page four of *Challenge One Journal, Part One*. This page explains the concept of denial and asks clients to indicate if they have behaved in any of the ways listed, which would be indicative of a tendency to deny drug problems. Some of the behaviors are also suggestive of other defense mechanisms.

3. When drug problems are serious, people around a drug-abusing individual may be

aware that something is wrong, while the drug abuser may still be in the dark. One way to break through denial or other defense mechanisms is to have clients request feedback from others about how they see things. In The Seven Challenges, *we have young people ask for feedback from adults and peers* about various aspects of their lives, on topics such as the harmfulness of their drug use. This technique of asking others for feedback is laced throughout the journals. Particularly relevant journal selections for recognizing harm from the use of drugs are in the *Challenge Three Journal* on pages five and six.

4. *All readings and journaling in Challenge Three are devoted to harm* from drug use. It is instructive about drug abuse and drug dependence. It helps young people look at harm they have already experienced, or potential harm. Examples of potential harm include drug overdose, engaging in high-risk behavior such as driving drunk (or under the influence of drugs), committing crimes, or engaging in sexual activity under the influence of alcohol or other drugs. As youth write in their journal, they are asked for their own ideas and opinions about the nature of drug abuse and the harm from their own drug using behavior. They themselves think about and record the harm — in black and white, and in their own handwriting.

5. *Challenge Five readings and journaling help young people think about potential harm in the future* if they continue to use drugs. It guides them in thinking ahead and anticipating future problems that might occur if their drug use continues at the current rate, or if it were to escalate. With drugs, it often takes time for the consequences to build up, kick in, or accumulate. The possibility of deferred consequences is especially true for youth because they are generally shielded from the immediate impact of their behavior by parents who provide food and shelter. As they get older and approach young adulthood, and must begin to think about providing for themselves, the reality of the harm hits home. They may find that they are behind in school, or out of school with no marketable job skills. Some parents inadvertently cause greater harm when they *enable* drug abuse. That is, they make special efforts to protect their children from the negative consequences of their behavior. They may make excuses for their children to school officials, or bail them out of legal problems or other trouble. In a sense, they help young people "get away with it." While protecting their children from the immediate consequences of their misbehavior, the drug problem continues to escalate until the harm is even more severe. In The Seven Challenges, clients are given an opportunity to think about where their drug use is leading them, and take note of whether this is consistent with their goals, dreams, values or hopes for themselves. Challenge Five helps young people look ahead and anticipate potential future harm, or cumulative harm, from their drug use.

6. *We use group sessions and group activities* so that young people get feedback from others. In particular, activities are designed to stimulate thinking and challenge young people to reflect on their own and each other's drug use. While participating in groups, feedback often comes from other peers, making it easier for young people to accept it.

7. *We use family sessions*, when appropriate, so young people can get feedback from family members about the harm from their drug use.

8. Counselors integrate information about the harm and dangers of drugs into *balanced drug education* (which does not discount drug "benefits"), presented in a creative and imaginative manner that helps engage teens and hold their attention.

9. We respectfully *give space for young people to think things through for themselves* and make their own appraisals in the counseling sessions. We know that youth are ambivalent about drugs and likely to lead with defensiveness. It is hard to admit to problems when pressured to attend counseling sessions. But secretly and privately, they have their concerns. We find ways to tap into their own concerns. Sometimes youth spontaneously discuss the harm from drugs, especially when they are not being pressured, backed into corners, and forced into a defensive position. Also, we respectfully ask youth for their own appraisals about harm. Instead of trying to make them admit they have problems, we give them a chance to reflect and make their own discoveries.

10. *We encourage peers in counseling sessions to seek feedback and give each other feedback about their drug use.*

11. After listening to youth and establishing rapport, *counselors in one-to-one or group sessions provide respectful feedback about the harm from drug use*. This should be handled in a non-argumentative fashion, with full awareness of the potential of generating resistance if not handled with attention to the adult/teen dynamic. Counselors say, for example: "Can I give you my opinion? This is my opinion about your drug use...and this is why... This is how I feel about what you said...."

12. Although harsh confrontation generates resistance, it is nevertheless important to confront misinformation, ignorance, defensiveness and defense mechanisms, such as denial, that prevent individuals from recognizing how they have been harmed by drugs. We probe and use *caring confrontation* in The Seven Challenges. Caring confrontation is a special case of respectful feedback, wherein the feedback is very strong and confrontational, but expressed in a respectful manner. We confront by expressing personal concern, rather than in the combative way that has typified the domain of drug treatment for adolescents. First we build up a solid relationship. Then we are better able to probe and confront youth about their drug use. Caring confrontation takes the form of "I statements" in which counselors share their perceptions, concerns, personal opinions or feelings about a youth's behavior. For example: "When I hear that you are driving down the street drunk, I am worried for you because you could hurt or even kill yourself, or someone else. I resent it, too, because I share those streets with you and I have a family. We are all at risk when you drive under the influence." Another example: "My opinion is that your drug use is already a problem and that if you keep doing what you are doing, you will be seriously hurting yourself and limiting your chances for a good future. That's how I see things...and I worry for you." Counselors can confront youth with strong opinions and strong feelings, as long as the tone is respectful

and the timing appropriate. Feelings are clearly stated as such. Opinions are also labeled as one's own opinions – not necessarily irrefutable truths. This leaves room for disagreement and open discussion. The intensity of the confrontation should correspond to the level of trust that has been built in the relationship.

13. *We empower individuals to feel that they could make changes.* When they feel powerful in this way, they are more willing to admit to problems. Empowerment is accomplished in a variety of ways in The Seven Challenges. Some examples are: by believing in young people — telling them that they will make their own choices in this program; by increasing their awareness of options (for instance, some young people grew up in situations in which all family members used drugs, and might not even realize that abstinence is an option); and by actually increasing the number of options available to young people (by solving problems and teaching social and emotional life skills). Another way we empower youth is by validating their experiences – helping them understand the people and situations that may have contributed to their drug use (see Challenge Four, just below). Validation is particularly important because it counteracts the disabling effects of shame. When people are ashamed of themselves, they are reluctant to admit to problems. When they can validate themselves – understand why they have behaved in the ways they have been behaving – they feel less shame. It is easier to admit to problems and acknowledge the harm from their drug use.

14. *Story telling and discussion* is another indirect way for clients to begin to look at harm from drug use.

15. Young people are moved to admit to problems and make changes in their lives as they *open their minds to optimism and dreams for themselves*, clarify their values, and use imagery to visualize a positive future.

The Seven Challenges Program does not rely on trying to convince young people that drugs have harmed them. Instead it is designed to use finesse to help young people get in touch with their own concerns and become more receptive to the constructive and respectful feedback of others, so if they have been harmed, they will realize it.

Counselors need to pay attention to avoid the pitfall of argumentation. They should pay attention to avoid the rebuttal cycle.

Similarly, counselors need to guard against playing the two most widely played games in drug counseling: "Try to convince me that drugs are dangerous" and "Try to convince me to quit." These games and various mutations of them do nothing to help young people gain awareness of the harm from drugs. Rather, they are sparring matches in which young people feel powerful because they can keep drug counselors at check, and sometimes even get them frustrated and all worked up. (This game, and how to avoid playing are discussed in more detail on pages 127-135.)

CHALLENGE FOUR CLINICAL SKILLS
EMPOWERING YOUNG PEOPLE WITH THE BIG PICTURE

VALIDATION

People sometimes feel so much shame about their behavior that they cannot readily admit to problems and go forward. Seeing themselves as defective, they are immobilized by self-blame. They blame themselves for everything, disregarding circumstances that at least partially explain what has happened to them. This state of mind can be particularly acute in young people in drug treatment programs who have been labeled as "druggies," "bad kids," "problem youth," or other pejoratives. No doubt they have had their problems and caused harm to themselves and others. However, shame and excessive self-blame are serious obstacles to self-growth. What young people really need is a compassionate attitude for understanding themselves and how their problems evolved.

One of the important Seven Challenges counseling skills is the ability to help people validate their behavior – to find explanations that make sense as to why they are behaving in the ways they have been behaving. Validation is helpful in efforts to overcome disabling self-blame. It is an important part of self-understanding that allows people to see how their behavior was shaped – which experiences had what impact upon them. With this understanding, they can accept their problems, and move forward to take responsibility for their lives and their future behavior.

Counselors in the Seven Challenges Program help young people put their problems and harmful behavior in perspective. Challenge Four, in particular, is written to promote this approach – to help them learn to validate themselves; that is, consider their family situation and whole environment, including opportunities they had (or were denied), and skills they were taught (and those they never had an opportunity to learn). This type of information reduces disproportionate self-blame. Most problem behavior can be understood in the context of hardships and other life experiences, and in terms of attitudes and skills that individuals never had an opportunity to learn.

When validated, individuals can see how a problem, or problem behavior, evolved from their life experiences, as in: "I can see why I have behaved this way. I see how my previous experiences have led to this outcome. It makes sense."

Consider the example of a fifteen-year-old girl who smokes marijuana every night before going to bed so she can fall asleep. Before she first started smoking, she would toss and turn in bed, sometimes for hours, trying to fall asleep. Her father left the family when she was very young. Her mother has struggled, trying to support this girl and her older brother. Mother drinks every night to drown her own pain. She has been involved with a whole series of men, some of whom have been abusive. She expects a lot of her children, but has practically no time to help them with school. The girl is always tense. She has been unable to live up to her mother's expectations. She is so tense at night that she can't sleep without smoking marijuana. Like so many other young people, she uses drugs to cope with problems and failures that are not entirely of her own making. She uses drugs to deal with pain because she cannot solve problems, or has not learned other ways of coping. Just like her mother, who is her role model, she uses drugs as a coping mechanism. Counselors can surely say, "I can see why you smoke marijuana before going to bed. It's the one way you had to fall asleep at night."

When validating clients, counselors offer their understanding of the context in which behavior occurs. Their statement might begin like the ones below:

- I can see why you are so angry.

- I can see why you have a problem with anger.

- I can see why you used drugs when you were angry.

- I can see why you are so anxious.

- I can see why you have had a problem with anxiety.

- I can see why you have used drugs when you were anxious.

- I can see why you have such pain.

- I can see why you used drugs when you were in pain.

And more:

- I can see why you have a problem with your temper.

- I can see why you have a problem with aggressive behavior.

- Yes, you have hurt yourself – and hurt others. I can see how this came to be.

FROM VALIDATION TO CONSTRUCTIVE CRITICISM AND SUPPORT

Counselor validation of client behavior serves as a bridge to constructive criticism. When clients feel that they are understood and respected by their counselors, they are more willing to hear and accept constructive criticism.

Consider the example of a boy who behaves aggressively to others. A counselor who knows the particular situation could validate a client in this way:

> You were brought up in an angry household. Your father had a serious temper problem. Your mother was seething with anger at him, but held it all in. You were mistreated, which made you angry, and never taught problem solving skills that could have helped you solve problems and reduce your own anger. You also were never taught appropriate ways of managing and expressing anger. That's why you came to behave in these aggressive ways, which are wrong.

This validation is the bridge to constructive criticism:

> Now that you know this is wrong, it is your responsibility to learn and practice new ways of coping with life, solving problems, and managing your anger and other emotions. You cannot continue to behave in aggressive ways. You can't go around hurting others.

Then counselors can provide the needed support:

> We can help you learn problem-solving skills so that you can prevent some of the things happening that make you angry. We can also teach you healthy ways to say what you feel and cope with angry feelings.

TAKING RESPONSIBILITY FOR ONE'S OWN BEHAVIOR

When validated, people are able to make sense of their behavior. They can explain it in context. They see how things came to be. This helps them move into the future and do the right thing – considering both their own needs and the rights of others.

Counselors should help with this as well. Here is an example:

> I think you would agree that what you did was wrong (or bad for you, or hurtful to others, or illegal, or unfair, or whatever). Now you need to do what is right. It is important to make changes.

Validation reduces disproportionate self-blame and helps people move forward and actually take responsibility for their behavior. Clients conclude: "Now I need to take responsibility for my behavior and make some changes."

Counselors sometimes have problems using the clinical skill of validation, especially some of those who work in the juvenile justice system. They are worried about appearing to accept, endorse, or enable unacceptable behavior. They confuse validation with justification. Justification occurs when people say that what has happened to them in their lives serves as a legitimate excuse for their own destructive behavior (to themselves and/or others). When people justify criminal behavior, it is classified as "criminal thinking."

Justification can also be described in this manner: Because of what others have done, I am *not* responsible for what I do now. Because I have been wronged, it is OK for me to do wrong things.

Wrong behavior should not be justified. When it is justified, then presumably it is OK to continue to behave in the same ways. Validation is different. It simply helps put the problem behavior in context. It does not justify the behavior. In fact, it empowers people to do what they should do, which is to solve the problem and behave properly. Rather than justifying the status quo, it energizes change.

CHALLENGE FIVE CLINICAL SKILLS
RE-ESTABLISHING OR DEVELOPING A FUTURE ORIENTATION

CHOICES

Challenge Five is about thinking ahead to the future. In this challenge, young people can think about what they want to have happen in the years to come. Counselors help them understand that they have choices and can make decisions and plans that will shape their future. An important clinical skill for Challenge Five is supporting clients in envisioning their future – and encouraging a sense of choice. This means helping them ask and answer the questions: What do I want to have happen in the years to come? What is important to me? What are my dreams for myself? What do I need to do to prepare for the future?

Many young people in drug treatment programs have lost sight of their dreams. They are alienated from their own core values. Sadly, many do not have an inspirational role model. Part of the work in this challenge is giving them a chance to rediscover or revise their dreams, articulate and clarify their values, and set goals for themselves.

DISCREPANCY

In Challenge Five young people are also given an opportunity to reflect upon where they are headed right now. Often there is a great deal of discrepancy between where they would like to go and where they seem to be headed. Young people can consider the connections they see between their drug use, or other behavior, and the likelihood of abiding by their values, reaching their goals, or fulfilling their ambitions. Helping clients recognize discrepancies[19] can be a powerful tool to motivate change.

FUTURE HARM

Harm from drug abuse is often experienced cumulatively – that is, in the long run. In this sense, some of the emphasis in Challenge Five clinical skills is directed toward anticipating future harm from drug use. In the short run, drugs feel good and can be an enjoyable recreational outlet. They can provide an easy escape from reality and responsibility. However, drug abuse often becomes an obstacle to school and career success, and to forming mature, loving relationships. This is important because adolescents are suppposed to be preparing for the future – preparing for adulthood. During the early and mid-teen years, adolescents should be thinking ahead. By approximately eighteen years of age an individual becomes a young adult in our culture and has certain responsibilities, such as providing for oneself or continuing with higher education. Teens also should be learning about mature loving relation-ships. However, during the early and mid-teen years, young people sometimes have a "don't care" attitude: "So what if I'm doing drugs and playing all the time? So what if I don't go to school?" The consequences only become evident as time passes without preparation for adulthood. Unless they get help in looking ahead, the risk is that they will become young adults without educational accomplishment and marketable job skills, and with little or no understanding of mature, loving relationships.

In The Seven Challenges we help young people look ahead and anticipate problems before they occur — when they are still in the best position to do something about them. Some of the clinical skills in Challenge Five are an extension of the Challenge Three skills: i.e., approaching harm from drug use in a sensitive, judicious way, without provoking defensiveness. We ask the question: "What will your life be like if you keep doing the things you are doing and keep heading in the direction you are headed?" The negative consequences can be further explored in the context of three other questions:

- What do you believe in?
- What sort of life do you want for yourself?
- What are your dreams?

HOPE AND OPTIMISM

Young clients with drug problems often lack a vision of a good life without drugs. If they were to stop using drugs, they imagine that their lives would be miserable. Therefore, a very important part of working with them is inspiring hope and optimism about the future. This includes helping them visualize a good life for themselves, and teaching them the skills and fostering the attitudes that would allow them to make this vision a reality. Counselors need to capture the imagination of these young people and show them that their efforts and hard work in making changes will pay off. Counselors need to help youth overcome problems that co-occur with drugs, and teach coping and life skills so that youth can have a good life without drugs.

Inspiring hope and optimism are crucial steps in the change process. People do not make changes if they think their lives would be worse from the changes. They make changes when they believe they will benefit and their lives will improve.

DEFERRED GRATIFICATION

In reviewing their own behavior and direction in life, many young people engaged in The Seven Challenges Program discover that they have a dilemma. They can focus on fun and pleasure in the present time, perhaps including the use of alcohol and other drugs. But the long-term consequences of this focus will be lack of preparation for the future and bleak times ahead. This recognition provides an opportunity to discuss the concept of deferred gratification, which means giving up some degree of immediate pleasure and gratification in exchange for greater benefits in the future.

CHALLENGE SIX CLINICAL SKILLS
MAKING REAL DECISIONS

A REAL DECISION TO QUIT

Over the years, drug counselors in a mad rush for abstinence have not only over-looked the preliminary groundwork that precedes the stage of decision-making, but also hastily breezed through decision making without attending to important details. Young people will often state their intent to change without fully understanding what this entails, without internal motivation, without a sense of commitment, and without adequate preparation to succeed in making the desired change.

The important clinical skills for Challenge Six are: (1) anticipating the likelihood of poorly grounded decisions to change; (2) knowing how to help clients think fully and carefully about their lives so that they make *informed, internally motivated and committed decisions*; (3) making sure that clients are sufficiently prepared for success, or at least have a roadmap for success, once they make their decisions; and (4) ensuring that the level of motivation to change is equal to the effort required to succeed. Before clients decide to quit using drugs, counselors must help them think carefully about what is motivating their decision, what it means to quit, and what preparations are necessary to be successful if they choose to follow through with the decision. The paragraphs below describe some of the pitfalls that counselors help their clients avoid or transcend.

Sometimes adolescent clients honestly say they are going to quit, but their reasons are largely external, such as, to make adults happy, or to stop the pressure. While these may be positive reasons to quit, they are not usually sufficient motivation for success. Young people need help finding additional, internal motivation for such changes, such as a reduction in harm from drugs, and envisioning a better life.

Another problem is "short term, fleeting motivation," which may be serious at the moment the intent to change is stated, but without significant substance. This sort of "weak decision" is sometimes made after a negative event occurs. For example, a boy huffing inhalants passes out and breaks a display counter in a department store. He is cut and bleeding. The police start asking questions. The next day he has no doubt in his mind: He plans to quit. He means it, too. A week or two passes, the memory fades, the cut heals, and he is back where he was before with regard to his drug usage — having no intent to stop. Adolescents need help distinguishing between fleeting desires to quit and a strong and serious commitment to change.

Often young people don't understand *the difference between wanting to quit and actually deciding to quit.* They don't fully realize that if they quit: (1) they will have to endure negative emotions they previously avoided by using drugs; (2) they will give up the good feelings and benefits from drugs; (3) they will need to make a whole lifestyle change because quitting is not a stand-alone decision. Not only will they have to stop using drugs, but they will also have to find new ways to have fun, new ways to cope with stress, new ways to manage anger and other emotions, and new ways to relax. They will probably have to drop some old friends and make some new ones.

Finally, young people say they will quit using drugs without realizing that in all likelihood this will be a huge struggle, perhaps not at the moment they state their intentions, but on all the occasions when they feel the urge to drink or "use." Quitting means not using even when they have their strongest urges, when the cues occur that make them want to use, for example, when friends show up with drugs; when they are very upset, sad or stressed out; and when they are angry. They also will not use drugs when fights erupt in their families.

Clients must understand what they are giving up and what they will face if they are going to make *informed* decisions about drugs. If decisions are not fully informed, clients are unlikely to be prepared for what lies ahead and unlikely to succeed. When they make decisions to change in the Seven Challenges Program, we want clients to be fully informed.

To further complicate matters, sometimes clients want to do something that is not a realistic option for them, such as continuing to use one drug, but quitting other drugs; or cutting back on their drug use, when they really need to quit. They also may want to cling to drug using friends when this would make it impossible to make the changes that they desire. In The Seven Challenges Program, they are given an opportunity to *realistically* look at their choices and decisions.

RETURNING HOME TO A FAMILY OR COMMUNITY WHERE DRUGS ARE USED

Some clients voice concerns about returning to families and communities where drugs are widely used. They may present this as an excuse for inaction. Counselors can validate their concern:

Yes, for you it will be harder than for others. To return to *your* environment puts you more at risk. You're at a disadvantage. It is like having one hand tied behind your back. So you must consider this reality.

Counselors can raise the issue of alternatives:

But, what's the option? To keep using drugs? You have to consider the consequences of this.

Finally, the discussion points to the importance of Challenge Six and to making informed, internally motivated, and committed decisions:

Knowing what you know about your situation shows how very important it is to carefully think through your decision about drugs. If you decide to stop using drugs, you will be returning to an environment that will be very difficult. It will not be easy to remain clean and sober. So, you must be very firm and committed to a decision to quit before making such a choice. You don't want to set yourself up for failure by deciding to do something, without realizing how hard it will be to succeed. Of course if you do decide to quit, you will have to work hard in planning and preparing for success, and we will work hard to support you.

CHALLENGE SEVEN CLINICAL SKILLS
RELAPSE PREVENTION AND LIFESTYLE ACTION

TAKING ACTION

After clients make fully informed, internally motivated, and committed decisions to change, they need to successfully follow through with implementing their decisions. Challenge Seven is the follow through and evaluation challenge. This is the action stage. With this challenge, counselors help clients make the desired changes. They help them recognize and appreciate their success. They also help them accept and learn from the inevitable setbacks and mistakes.

Most drug treatment for adolescents has pretty much *started* with behavioral change. Young people are rushed through decision-making. Those who do not flee and do not dig in their heels will soon say that they intend to "quit using." Then they are taught how to be drug-free, through *relapse prevention*. Unfortunately they are generally taught how to be drug-free before they really decided they wanted to be drug free, knew what it entailed to be drug-free, and/or laid the groundwork for success in this endeavor.

It is different with the Seven Challenges. The first five challenges lay the groundwork for change. In Challenge Six, young people make decisions about changes in two realms; with regard to drug use, and with regard to various co-occurring and lifestyle issues. Challenge Seven, Part One, is follow through on lifestyle changes. Challenge Seven, Part Two, is relapse prevention, which is follow through on drug decisions. Because there is a good deal of published information widely available about relapse prevention,[20] this manual will not offer detailed instructions on this topic. The Seven Challenges Program follows mainstream approaches to relapse prevention, but with the added benefits of: (1) building upon work with previous challenges and (2) taking a holistic perspective that makes connections between lifestyle changes and drug changes.

RELAPSE PREVENTION

State of the art relapse prevention involves helping clients identify the people, places, emotions, situations, thoughts, and things that are likely to stimulate relapse. Sometimes these stimuli are referred to as "cues" or "triggers." It involves making plans to prevent relapse and learning how to avoid, escape, or cope with such triggers. It also involves determining to whom to turn for support and inspiration in making changes. In part, relapse prevention means learning to deal with situational pressure. It also means learning to counter one's own cognitive messages (self-talk) and urges to use drugs.

To some extent, certain high-risk situations — which might tempt an individual to use drugs — can be avoided. For example, young people can physically avoid certain situations, such as parties where they know drugs will be present. They can also avoid temptation by solving problems which, if not solved, could be triggers to drug use. However, avoidance alone is insufficient. Drugs and drug triggers cannot entirely be avoided. So, young people must learn to successfully cope with challenging situations in which they might be exposed to drugs or drug triggers. They need to recognize warning signs such as thoughts, feelings, and behaviors that could lead to a relapse. They need to develop their resistance skills. They need to gain control over their urges when they are exposed to drug cues. Counselors prepare them by providing assistance in making predetermined plans of action for coping with high risk situations; providing opportunities to role-play refusing drugs; and providing practice in answering cognitive messages that urge them to use. People who stop abusing drugs may suffer minor setbacks involving single incidents of drug use or brief periods of use, known as lapses. Or, they could suffer more serious setbacks, known as relapses, in which they use drugs at high levels and lose substantial ground. Accepting the inevitability of mistakes and setbacks, and learning from them — are the healthy alternatives to what is known as the Abstinence Violation Effect,[21] in which people who slip from their sobriety feel defeated, throw up their hands, regress to pre-contemplation, and give up.

Some young people who are inclined toward spirituality and who accept the concept of "surrendering to a higher power" will turn to 12-step groups for support of their abstinence. This is a good match for them. There are other community groups and recovery groups that support abstinence, such as Smart Recovery and Women for Sobriety. Clients also identify specific people to whom they will turn for support when they feel the urge to drink or use drugs, or for other types of help, of if they suffer a lapse or relapse.

USING WORK FROM EARLIER CHALLENGES IN RELAPSE PREVENTION

The Seven Challenges Model offers some unique tools in implementing successful relapse prevention plans. With The Seven Challenges Process, young people are learning relapse prevention tools before they commit to making changes. In Challenge Two young people identify the needs they are meeting, or trying to meet, through their drug use. This provides a window onto the situations in which they are likely to experience triggers to drink or get high. For example, if they learned in Challenge Two that they used drugs to relax when they were stressed, then surely a trigger for relapse would be situations in which they would be feeling stressed. Hence, reviewing the work from Challenge Two can be used to identify risk situations, and to make relapse prevention plans. Challenges Three and Five provide information about the harm and potential harm from drug use. In relapse prevention, many people keep a reminder list of the harm they suffered from drug use to reinforce their efforts to stay clean and sober, particularly at times that they may feel urges to use. This list can easily be prepared from reviewing previous work in Challenges Three and Five. They can also review Challenge Five to remind themselves of the type of future they want, and Challenge Six to consider their level of committment to change.

LIFESTYLE ACTION

While most drug treatment for youth has focused narrowly on teaching young people to be drug free, the Seven Challenges Counseling approach differs in that treatment goals are broadened to include lifestyle action as part of a bigger process of change. The program is holistic. In using The Seven Challenges, we are not simply trying to overcome a negative behavior (drug abuse); we are equally seeking to help young people take action to make a better life for themselves. This includes work in solving co-occurring problems, gaining mastery over one's life, and learning and implementing new life skills. This prepares young people for relapse prevention, even before they have decided to change. To be drug free, they will need to solve problems and use new life skills to satisfy their needs and desires without drugs. Personal problems and difficult situations which could stimulate relapse, or be a precursor to relapse, are identified and remedied all through The Seven Challenges Program – starting early in the change process.

Once young people do decide to make important changes in their lives, every effort is made in this program to help them connect with support people; appreciate all forms of success; and accept and learn from setbacks and mistakes.

IMPLEMENTATION

HOW TO INTRODUCE THE SEVEN CHALLENGES PROGRAM TO YOUTH

Below is a model statement of how to introduce The Seven Challenges Program to young clients. A good orientation to the program can help undo negative expectations about drug treatment. For maximal effectiveness, a good introduction should be delivered with enthusiasm.

"I think you're going to like The Seven Challenges Program. It's probably different from what you expect from a drug treatment program, and if you've been in a program before, you will see that it really is quite different.

"I think you'll see it's a respectful program in that no one tells you what to do or how to lead your life. It's designed to help you think through your drug use, and your life, *for yourself*. In this program, no one exaggerates the dangers of drugs or tells you what to do about drugs. You make your own decisions.

"The program is based on the experiences and ideas of young people who prevented or overcame serious drug problems. What these successful young people all had in common was that they *challenged* themselves and each other to think clearly about their lives, and about their use of alcohol and other drugs. That's why the program is called The Seven Challenges. Alcohol and other drugs are powerful stuff. People who use drugs really need to challenge themselves to think carefully and clearly about what they are doing.

"In The Seven Challenges Program we do everything we can to make it safe for you to talk openly and honestly with us about your life, and about alcohol and other drugs. Many young people lie about their drug use. One reason they lie is because when they told the truth to some adults in the past, they only got into more trouble. We want to make it safe for you to tell the truth. That's our responsibility — to make this program safe.

"I think you'll like The Seven Challenges because, you'll see, it gives you room to do your own clear headed thinking. We trust you and give you an opportunity to think for yourself and make your own wise decisions."

SEVEN CHALLENGES SESSIONS

Because books and journals are part of The Seven Challenges Program, it may seem that these resources *are* the program, and that counseling sessions would simply involve clients reading from *The Seven Challenges* book and writing in their journals. This is not the case. Although the book and journals are valuable resources, they do not by any means constitute the whole program. The program is about young people using the Seven Challenges process to move through the various stages of change – looking at their lives; making decisions and then following through with them. This is accomplished to a large extent during counseling/educational sessions, in conjunction with use of the published materials.

The Seven Challenges Program does not prescribe what takes place in each counseling session. Good drug counseling is responsive to the needs and interests of the clients. Often the best sessions revolve around issues that are on the minds of young clients at the moment. Youth have issues they want to discuss. They will bring them into the open when we create a safe and supportive climate that allows them to talk openly. We discuss these issues as they arise, as well as plan and prepare additional activities that address the relevant issues. Not all critical issues will arise spontaneously. Counselors must also know, and continually evaluate, which additional topics and issues need to be discussed in individual or group sessions, and when to lead in the direction indicated.

The focus of counseling sessions will include evaluating drug use and making decisions about drugs. It will equally include consideration of the whole person — his or her history, situation, and circumstances. Counseling sessions are also geared to teaching skills that increase options, such as problem solving, stress reduction, and anger management.

Another requirement of the program is that all one-to-one sessions, group discussions, and other activities need to be referenced to The Seven Challenges process. Young people need to understand how any particular discussion, problem-solving work, or activity relates specifically to The Seven Challenges Process. (How to do this is discussed on pages 75-76.)

A WORKING SEVEN CHALLENGES SESSION DEFINED

In The Seven Challenges Program, youth are not required to say they will quit using drugs. Nevertheless, they are required to think things through and reach their own conclusions: to actively look at their lives, learn life skills to increase options, consider options, make decisions, and act on the decisions. This means that counseling cannot be simply a passive experience. *Clients must work. Sessions must be working sessions. Groups must be working groups.*

In working sessions, individuals will engage in one or more of the following activities:

- *actively reflect upon their lives (thoughts, feelings, behavior, beliefs, values, choices; goals, history and current situation);*

- *problem-solve about their lives;*

- *plan, initiate, or evaluate behavior changes; or*

- *participate in structured activities that teach a skill or increase self understanding.*

Clients do not spontaneously understand what it means to have working sessions. Many people, including youth and adults, have some vague idea that counseling means you "just talk." In fact, most expect a relatively passive experience in which (1) counselors tell them precisely what to do and/or (2) clients talk about whatever pops into their minds. So counselors have to teach what it means to participate in working sessions. These sessions are focused. Clients have responsibilities. We ask young people to think about and discuss issues in their lives that are most important to them and require reflection. We also ask them to take a problem-solving approach – to consider what problems are occurring in their lives – and to work on solving them, and on changing behaviors that they feel need to be changed. We encourage youth to think about important issues and problems before sessions so they have some idea about what they want to "work on." Other ideas about what to work on may occur to them in the midst of a counseling session. If clients have trouble identifying issues that require work, we help them learn how to do this during sessions. In addition to client-initiated work, we explain that counselors will sometimes bring an agenda item or activity to the session.

Throughout the counseling process, counselors continue to remind youth what it means to work; and reinforce a working agenda by asking, "Who wants to work today?" (in a group) and "What do you want to work on today?" They redirect individuals away from other types of interactions, and toward work.

When groups first form, it is a substantial challenge to establish a working norm. Eventually, however, the norm is established and new group members can more readily assimilate the concept of working sessions as they observe the process in a mature, working group.

Insistence on "working sessions" has special significance in drug counseling for adolescents because sessions with this population are often plagued by the games of "Try to prove that I've been harmed by drugs," or "Try to make me quit using drugs," or variations of these games. When these games are played, sessions become interminable arguments and power struggles. In individual counseling, a whole session can be spent playing one or more versions of this game. In group sessions, one teen after another will engage in this type of game-playing, often with willing counselors who are both eager to prove that drugs are dangerous, and dedicated to convincing young people that they should quit. Counselors never win the arguments, but often end up feeling angry and bitter toward the youth who play games. They may express this resentment with angry criticism, or by imposing consequences on youth. But the youth who play the games get lots of attention and feel very powerful. Their victory is secured when they bring counselors to a state of frenzied anger. These games must be avoided. These games and how to avoid playing them are discussed in detail on pages 127-135 of this manual.

One way to avoid the games is to be sure to have a working group or (working individual sessions). Establish the expectation of working sessions clearly — and stick to it. When young people try to lure counselors into the games, counselors should be clear that their job is not to convince youth of anything or to make them do anything – and then invite the youth to participate by working on their personal issues in group – which is the purpose of the group.

When counselors are not well prepared for group sessions, they are more vulnerable to these games, which do structure time, but sadly, waste it. Satisfactorily preparing for sessions can go a long way to ensure a working group.

PLANNING AND PREPARING FOR COUNSELING SESSIONS

Because The Seven Challenges is not a cookie-cutter program with pre-scripted protocols, it is up to the counselor to plan and structure each and every session. This requires preparation time to think about what work would be most appropriate for an individual, or a family, or for a group, in each meeting. Initial preparation may include gathering information from client histories and ancillary sources, such as family members, other providers, and other members of a treatment team. In on-going sessions, consideration should be given to the big picture – what has already been covered in counseling and what needs to be covered – and to current issues raised in recent sessions. Family and group dynamics need to be considered in family and group sessions. Milieu issues are highly relevant in residential settings.

In group sessions, young people either (a) reflect upon, or problem solve, with regard to an issue they have identified, and/or (b) work on behavior change, or (c) participate in structured activities. Most sessions are structured to allow youth to bring up issues they want to address during the group. Some counselors begin with a brief "check-in" period, during which time clients may be asked if they want to "work on" an issue that they have mentioned. Also, group members can be asked after a check-in (or a planned initial activity): "Who wants to work in group today?" With this flexible approach, counselors give young people an opportunity to problem solve about issues of their choice. If no one wants to problem solve, the back-up plan is to work with pre-selected activities that the counselor initiates. It is a good idea to have several activities in mind for a particular session, with the final choice of activity, or activities, being based on group response. Sometimes in planning sessions, counselors decide ahead of time that a certain activity is so essential that they will stick with it, regardless of the more immediate issues raised by group members.

TEACHING LIFE SKILLS

A premise of The Seven Challenges Program is that young people use drugs to meet personal, social, emotional, and psychological needs — and to cope with life. Therefore, an important part of drug treatment is to empower clients to meet their needs and cope with life without drugs. That is why much of the work in individual, group, and family counseling sessions will concern problem solving on issues other than drugs.

In a comprehensive Seven Challenges Program, co-occurring problems must be addressed. Counselors must be prepared to deal with mental health issues, as well as drug issues.

Also, many sessions are dedicated to teaching life skills, such as anger management, stress reduction, relationship communications, impulse control, and the like. Examples of sessions of this sort are included in The Seven Challenges Activity Book. Numerous other resources are available for life skills training and should be incorporated as part of Seven Challenges counseling sessions. As you will see below, counselors help clients see the connections between each and every activity and The Seven Challenges Process.

RELATE ACTIVITIES, DISCUSSIONS, AND PROBLEM SOLVING SESSIONS TO THE SEVEN CHALLENGES

Because The Seven Challenges Program does not prescribe specific counseling sessions, sound clinical judgment dictates what would be the most beneficial activity in given groups at a given time. However: *The art of leading a successful Seven Challenges Group depends to a great extent on the ability of a counselor to relate the group activities of the day to the Seven Challenges Process.*

Making the links to The Seven Challenges is important because this is an empowerment model. Young people are not told what to do about drugs or their lives. We do not want them to feel we are "fixing" them or trying to control their behavior. Rather we let them know that we use The Seven Challenges as a framework to help them make their own decisions, and to empower them with new skills. We want young people to see the relevance of their efforts to the various aspects of making wise, healthy decisions. We want them to understand that they are active participants in a thoughtful process – and to see how each activity relates to their effort in making good decisions. Therefore, counselors should make connections between the work focus of each session – whether it involves structured activities, active reflection upon one's life, problem solving work, or behavior change – and the various challenges in The Seven Challenges. The Seven Challenges Poster can be used as a helpful visual aid in helping clients see the connection between their work and the challenges that can be displayed in front of them.

With structured activities, connections with the Seven Challenges' process can be discussed either before beginning the activity, during it, and/or at the end. Similarly, all discussions and problem solving work should be put in the context of the Seven Challenges. Most discussions or activities can be related to any number of challenges. For example, consider a session in which youth discuss stress and coping with stress, and then listen to a relaxation tape. Some of the links to challenges include the following:

- Many people use drugs to relax when they are tense. Looking at reasons for drug use is a Challenge Two issue.

- Some young people lived with a great deal of stress in their family and community and many never had an opportunity to learn relaxation skills. Making this connection is a Challenge Four issue.

- If clients decide to quit using drugs (Challenge Six), they will need other ways to cope with stress. Relaxation skills are a way to cope.

- If clients are working on relapse prevention, they will need to anticipate stressful situations, and plan to avoid, escape, or cope with them (Challenge Seven).

- A relaxation session is also a team builder and trust builder (As such, it is a Challenge One issue.)

Counselors can point out the connections between a particular activity and relevant challenges, or, they might involve youth in thinking this through for themselves. For example: "Today we are doing an exercise on anger management. In what ways can you relate this to The Seven Challenges? Explain the relevance you see between this activity and some of the challenges."

Another example: "Today we are doing an activity about what you expect your drug use might look like in the future – six months from now, one year from now, and in 10 years. You will see that this is relevant in different ways to different challenges. It is especially relevant to Challenge Five because this challenge is about looking ahead to the future. Challenge Five is: We thought about where we seemed to be headed, where we wanted to go, and what we wanted to accomplish.

As clients engage in problem-solving and changing behavior, connections between the work and The Seven Challenges should be made. For example, a girl might be problem solving about family issues. Counselors can help the girl see the connection between the family problems and her use of drugs. For example: This could be a Challenge Two issue (using to deal with feelings about her family); a Challenge Three issue (the way she is harming herself or family from drug use); a Challenge Four issue (the responsibility of self and others – i.e., her family in contributing to her drug and other problems); a Challenge Five issue (future harm from her drug use); and a Challenge Six and Seven issue (the family as a potential trigger for drug use if she were to quit using).

In leading groups, counselors can draw upon the activities presented in *The Seven Challenges Activity Book*. In that book, various connections are made between the activities and the challenges. Often, however, counselors will be leading problem solving work, or using other activities they originated themselves, or found elsewhere. On these occasions, they will need to think about, and help young people see, the links to the different challenges.

ONGOING ORIENTATION TO THE SEVEN CHALLENGES

To help clients make the most of this program, we have already discussed the importance of providing an initial orientation to The Seven Challenges. Beyond that, in all counseling sessions, the challenges serve as an on-going framework to help young people think about their lives and drug use, make decisions for themselves, and follow through with their decisions. Finally, another important way to help young people understand the process is to occasionally have sessions in which counselors simply discuss all of the seven challenges, or focus on one or more of them. The idea is to make sure that young people fully understand The Seven Challenges Process – see it as one piece — and can use it effectively in their decision-making. As previously stated, The Seven Challenges Poster is an excellent visual aid for keeping the process in the forefront of clients' minds.

NUTS AND BOLTS FOR GROUPS

GROUP SIZE

The number of participants in a Seven Challenges group is not prescribed. Experience has shown that a small group of six to eight is optimal, but considerably larger groups with as many as 12 members are sometimes necessary, and can succeed. When possible, it helps to have co-leaders work as a team, especially with larger groups. This arrangement also allows for flexibility in terms of dividing the group, or meeting individually with youth.

LENGTH OF GROUP SESSION

Groups of about one hour length have been found to be optimal. In intensive outpatient programs, with three hour meetings, or longer, sessions can be broken into smaller segments, such as: A one hour Seven Challenges Group; followed by one hour of recreation or yoga or something artistic or musical; followed by an hour for working with books and journals. Although the goal is to accomplish serious work in the group, successful adolescent groups incorporate humor and light heartedness. Whenever possible, structured activities should involve movement from one's seat. In long, intensive outpatient sessions, refreshments are served.

GROUP COMPOSITION

One of the most difficult challenges in leading group counseling sessions is the beginning, when group norms are first established. This is especially challenging in work with adolescents with drug problems because so many participants are mandated to treatment and have negative expectations about what will occur. An important initial objective is to "win the consciousness" of the group, so that a critical mass of members feel good about participating, see the value of the work, and understand that they have become part of an effective and powerful "working group." *To avoid starting anew each time with a whole set of resistant youth, it is ideal to have an on-going, open group in which new members join as others leave.* In on-going groups, peers who have come to value the group will work as allies with counselors in helping new members adjust. They will assist in welcoming new peers, helping them value the experience and understand how things work in the group.

In on-going groups, different members will be working on different challenges, with some being further along than others. They will also be in different stages of change. This is workable because almost all group discussions and activities can be related to various challenges and made relevant to individuals in different stages of change. In addition to helping new group members adjust, veteran youth will have an opportunity to serve as positive peer leaders — an experience that works well with The Seven Challenges Program.

For administrative reasons, it is not always possible to have on-going groups. In some situations, young people enter as cohorts and proceed through the program together at the same pace. Although the program can be done this way, this approach does create the problem of starting over with each group of cohorts. It also drastically reduces opportunities for individualization of the program.

STARTING SEVEN CHALLENGES GROUPS

As mentioned above, one of the most difficult tasks in group therapy with substance abusing youth is to establish norms in new groups. With The Seven Challenges, starting a new group means creating a climate in which group members can talk openly and honestly, and feel supported in making positive changes in their lives. It also means teaching about working sessions. Group leaders need to "win" group members over to this sort of positive approach. They have to "win the consciousness" of the group.

Because of the strong resistance of many young people to drug counseling, counselors would be well advised to start with a small group of the most willing and eager youth, whenever this is possible. An alternative approach is to start with whomever comes, with the intention of asking some individuals to leave temporarily if they are consistently resisting, opposing, disrupting, or interfering with the effort of others who are committed to establishing a working group. Usually counselors meet with new clients individually before the first group session, to build the relationship, and help orient and prepare them for the program. In some settings, there may be a number of preliminary meetings. This is one way to try to generate "buy in" before meeting in the group setting. In some situations, counselors must work with, and persist with, all youth who are placed in their groups. Gradually they will win the consciousness of the group.

Counseling finesse is required to minimize attention on individuals who resist counseling, and to avoid time-consuming power struggles with them. Instead, skilled counselors focus and direct most of their attention toward those most willing and committed to work.

When groups first start, and as new people join, it is important to orient new members to:

- the purpose and philosophy of the Seven Challenges Program;
- the role of the counselor in this program;
- the expectations placed on group members;
- the concept of a working group;
- and the rules that are established to provide the most secure possible work environment for the group.

POSITIVE INTRODUCTION TO THE PROGRAM

One top priority with new program participants is to explain The Seven Challenges in a positive way that will lower resistance and generate interest, curiosity, or even excitement about what lies ahead. This means talking about the purpose of the program, which is to empower young people with an opportunity to think about their drug use and their lives, and to make their own wise decisions. (See How to Introduce The Seven Challenges Program on page 71.) This also means trying to undo negative expectations by being clear that this is *not* a program that tries to dictate or control their lives. As youth continue in The Seven Challenges, they will need to be reminded of how the process works and continually oriented to the idea that we are giving them options and freedom of choice.

Initial group sessions should incorporate activities and discussions that feel non-threatening, so that participants feel safe and begin to build trust in the adults, the peers, the counseling process and the program. Some young people may be eager to work on their issues from the very beginning and should be given this opportunity. Others must be given a warm welcome and ample time to check it out. Initial resistance should be expected. Counselors should simply roll with the resistance.[22] (See also Guest Status on page 81.)

POSITIVE INTRODUCTION OF COUNSELING ROLE

It is also important that counselors *introduce themselves in a positive way* – one that will undo negative expectation about their role. Thus counselors can say:

> "You don't have to say you're going to quit using drugs in this group. We are not here to make you quit using drugs, or to try to control your behavior. Instead of telling you what to do and how to lead your lives, we will be supporting you in your own efforts to make a good life for yourselves. For this to happen, we want to do all that we can to make this group a safe place for you to think and talk freely. For example, you're going to see that you won't get in trouble with us in here for saying that you like drugs, or want to keep using them. We assume many of you feel that way. There are, however, some expectations that we will explain and rules that have been established, mainly for your own protection."

Counselors must be crystal clear in presenting this point of view. First, counseling needs to be differentiated from other milieu issues. Counseling is a free-thinking process. It requires a free-thinking zone for the mind. The only behavior control issue in a counseling situation should be that individuals follow the rules of the group. However, adolescent drug counseling often takes place within settings that have various other types of behavioral expectations. In correctional or residential settings, a good deal of an individual's behavior will be controlled. There are extensive and serious limits and rules. In these settings, counselors can clarify, "There are many rules here, where you live. But no one can, or should, control your mind. You are free to think and feel whatever comes in your mind. In counseling sessions, you are free to express what you feel, within the limits of group rules. This is an opportunity to put your thinking out in the open – and get some support in thinking things through."

WEARING TWO HATS

Ideally counselors will stick with their counseling function while counseling, and will not also be the ones responsible for day-to-day discipline (although, for administrative reasons, this is not always possible). When counselors also have responsibility for monitoring and controlling milieu behavior, they need to differentiate this task from their work in conducting counseling sessions. In a sense, they are wearing two different hats and should be very clear about which hat they are wearing at any given moment. In the milieu setting the priority is appropriate behavior, and the adult has behavioral control responsibility. In the counseling setting, the focus is on creating an environment in which free thinking can occur.

Other staff members — with titles such as line staff, youth workers, or psych techs — may have the reverse situation. Most of the day they are responsible for monitoring and controlling milieu behavior. But they may participate in group counseling sessions, or have conversations of a counseling nature. They, too, will be wearing two different hats. As counselors, they must encourage, permit, and tolerate free thinking. When they are in the milieu, they wear their behavior control hats.

It is a real discipline for the adults to keep the roles separate. Youth will surely need convincing that counseling sessions are different from the very controlled atmosphere of most of the rest of their day. So, adults must be doubly aware to wear the counseling hat, when in the counseling session.

WHAT'S EXPECTED OF GROUP MEMBERS IN A WORKING GROUP

Another top priority is to introduce the idea of a working group to group members:

> "We are not here to make you behave in any special way. We do not require that you have to say that you are going to quit using drugs to be in this group (see *addendum*, just below for exceptions). We don't tell you what to do with your lives. You have to make your own choices. However, there is one requirement: that you look closely at your life, think hard about it, and address problems that are affecting you. You do have to 'work on yourself' in counseling sessions. In other words, we must have working groups (or individual or family sessions). In working sessions, you will either be thinking carefully about your life, participating in structured group activities, problem solving about your life; or making behavior changes in your life that you want to make. Our expectation is that you will engage in this effort; come to sessions prepared to work; and hopefully, support others in their efforts."

Addendum to the above statement: The clients do not have to say they are going to quit using drugs. Some drug counseling is based on the premise that an individual will be abstinent in order to qualify for the services. This could be a condition of probation, or a condition for participation in a drug court program, or simply an agency requirement. (For more detailed discussion of using The Seven Challenges under these conditions, see Working on Two Levels on pages 115-125.)

The Seven Challenges Manual ©2004 Robert Schwebel, Ph.D.

When courts insist upon abstinence, counselors should not assume the responsibility of making adolescents quit. Counselors are still charged with helping young people think through their problems for themselves. The difference is that there are external forces at work (the courts) that insist upon abstinence and might impose consequences if young people do not comply. This will surely influence and have significant bearing on youth efforts at making their own decisions. When agencies, themselves, require abstinence, counselors cannot say, "You don't have to say you're going to quit." Rather this becomes a requirement and will undoubtedly increase the likelihood of youth responding with lies and resistance.

GUEST STATUS: TIME TO ADJUST AND CHECK US OUT

Although the expectation is that youth will open up and start working in the counseling sessions, it is not realistic to think that this will happen immediately. It may take time for them to feel comfortable with the process. Counselors want to help them feel comfortable. One way to do this is to offer "guest treatment" and provide "guest status" to new program participants. This idea is inspired by discussion of the "visitor-host" type of relationship in solution-focused therapy.[23] In a sense, guest status means recognizing that someone new has entered our domain. They are like guests in our home. We want to greet them warmly, help them feel comfortable, and give them a chance to adjust. This is especially apt in the Seven Challenges because many youth enter drug treatment with negative expectations. They are mistrustful at first, primed to resist counseling, and not very receptive to the idea of discussing personal matters. They will be watchful – trying to determine whether the program is a safe place or not. They need an opportunity to lay back a bit, observe what happens, and get acquainted with the program before they are willing to fully commit themselves. Extending "guest status" is a way to remove pressure from new group members or individual clients. With guest status, new clients do not have to work in initial sessions. Counselors avoid making demands or pressuring with too many questions that could be perceived as demands. This does not mean that they can be disruptive. But they can be quiet and outwardly uninvolved. They should not be pressured to immediately talk openly about themselves beyond a basic introduction. They can have time to "check things out" and develop a sense of comfort. They can ask questions to understand how things work.

GROUP RULES

In orienting youth to The Seven Challenges, it is important that counselors explain about safety and protection in group sessions. This includes group rules and how leaders will operate. Some group rules are non-negotiable and essential to success in The Seven Challenges. Others may be selected by group leaders, preferably with input from group members.

Two basic assumptions in Seven Challenges groups are: (1) that members will work in the group and (2) that the group will be safe so that members are free to open up and talk honestly.

To make groups a safe place to work, these are the rules:

- No physical abuse or violence

- No threatening remarks

- No put downs, insults, or foul language

- Respect for each other, group leader, and property

- No interruptions. One person talks at a time

- No horseplay

- Hands and feet kept to yourself

- Issues discussed in group stay in group (are not repeated outside of the group)

- Information about a peer can never be used as a weapon, either in person with that peer, or by gossiping or talking with others outside of group

Counselors have the responsibility of protecting group members. The principles of good group leadership are applied in enforcing these rules. Counselors must be convincing about their intent to enforce these rules, and then diligently and consistently enforce them. Otherwise the group process will work counter to the group purpose. Counselors must respond to violations appropriately – interrupting and stopping the misbehavior, and imposing sanctions when needed.

All but the last two rules listed above apply to behavior within group. The last two mostly happen outside group, although using information about a peer as a weapon can also occur in the group setting. It is particularly essential to back up the last rule with very strong sanctions. *To use information about a peer as a weapon is actually a form of bullying. Just as we would not for a moment tolerate physical aggression in groups, we should equally be clear that we will not tolerate verbal aggression. No bullying, of any sort, is allowed. If information is used as a weapon, the sanctions should be as strong as the ones that apply to physical abuse or violence. In addition to other sanctions, clients may be expelled from group for breaking this rule, and may have to apply for readmission. Unless this level of protection is provided, group members will be reluctant to reveal anything personal about themselves.* The guiding principle is straightforward common sense: If we are going to ask clients top open up and make themselves vulnerable, then we are obligated to provide safety and protection.

CONFIDENTIALITY

The Seven Challenges Program must be set up so that young people do not get in trouble when they tell the truth. Otherwise they will be much less likely to talk openly about themselves. Every effort should be made to ensure this practice. This is the historic basis for confidentiality. "Protected communication" is a trade off, with both costs and benefits. Protected information is *not* disclosed to others who may have interest in knowing the information. However, the protection from disclosure provides an individual with an opportunity to get help on the behavior that otherwise might be hidden. Drug counseling has special federal provisions to protect confidentiality, above and beyond the protection provided for other types of counseling and psychotherapy. It has long been recognized that people are more likely to hide substance abuse problems if they believe they will get in trouble for revealing them. Clearly teens will be more likely to talk openly about their drug use if they are confident they will not be punished for what they reveal.

There are factors that mitigate against confidentiality. For example, when staff works as a team in treatment, it is less than ideal for one person to withhold information from others. Sometimes we simply must inform the team. Also, there may be rules, for example in a private school, that prohibit drug use. Withholding information from colleagues is problematic. Confidentiality also becomes an issue when clients are on probation. Sometimes, therefore, all information cannot be withheld. Nonetheless, whenever possible it is best to avoid mandatory disclosure of specific content of sessions because it seriously compromises the effectiveness of a program. Even mandatory disclosures can be clearly limited in terms of what is revealed. In fairness, youth need to know the limits of the confidentiality from the very onset of their counseling.

With regard to confidentiality about drug use, it is important to recognize that there are creative ways to keep some channels open, while gaining maximum confidence. Sometimes courts do their own drug testing, which removes the burden of counselors reporting drug use. Instead, the courts monitor, test, and detect drug use. Sometimes arrangements can be made so that progress in treatment is measured by attendance, participation and effort in counseling, rather than by whether or not there is one or more incidents of drug use. Also, some schools or other institutions are willing to allow counselors to maintain confidentiality about drug use so that their work can be more effective and youth will seek and accept help. School administration still can use drug testing if they need to know about drug use.

SEVEN CHALLENGES SERVICES

Unless the counseling modality is individual sessions, the core service in the Seven Challenges Program is a regular Seven Challenges Group, sometimes referred to as a Seven Challenges Discovery Group. These groups can meet any number of times a week, depending upon the intensity of the program. In most settings, clients are also offered Journaling Group, which is structured time during which they can read from *The Seven Challenges* and write in their *Seven Challenges Journals*. With individual counseling, counselors sometimes have clients stay an hour after their sessions to read and write in their journals.

Young people who commit to stopping their drug abuse need help with relapse prevention. To provide this, another important service in a comprehensive program is a Seven Challenges Lifestyle Action Group (LA Group). These are special groups, in addition to a basic Seven Challenges Discovery Group, for individuals who have demonstrated effort in the program and made decisions about taking decisive action about their drug use — and want time for problem solving assistance that is not diluted by the participation of other group members who are still trying to make decisions, and perhaps waffling on whether to take action. This group encompasses what is generally referred to as Relapse Prevention Groups, and more. In these groups clients work on their relapse prevention plan, with regard to drugs. We do not call this a relapse prevention group, however, because youth sometimes react unfavorably to that concept ("You're doubting me"). They react more favorably to the idea that they can take control of their life through lifestyle action. Also the groups are more than just relapse prevention groups. We know that people who choose to stop abusing drugs also need to make other changes in their lives. In these groups young people can get extra help on making these other behavioral changes, such as overcoming anger problems, learning to make drug-free friends, solving specific problems at home, learning specific life skills or making specific lifestyle changes, or whatever other behavior they have committed to changing.

The LA Group prepares participants for action, helps them take action, and helps them evaluate the effectiveness of their action. Members of the LA Group would still attend at least one Seven Challenges Discovery Group per week, but could substitute a LA Group for an additional Discovery session.

Trauma Recovery is another important basic service in a comprehensive Seven Challenges Program. This is necessary because many youth with drug problems have been victims in their lifetime of sexual or physical abuse, or have been traumatized by being witnesses to violence, sometimes in their own homes. Because The Seven Challenges emphasizes creating a safe environment and encouraging honesty, counselors in the program often become the first one to hear about – and report – abuse. Therefore, it is important to be prepared with appropriate services.

In implementing a comprehensive program, some agencies develop special groups to teach various life and coping skills. Or, life and coping skill training can be incorporated as part of the Discovery and LA Groups.

Parent and family services are another important consideration in adolescent drug abuse treatment. All parents — or the other adults who care for youth – should be provided with an orientation to The Seven Challenges Program. Parent education and family services, discussed below, are integrated in program whenever possible and advisable.

ORIENTING PARENTS TO THE SEVEN CHALLENGES

Youth live with parents or other adults who care for them. They are not at liberty to leave. Some youth are temporarily out of their homes in residential or correctional settings, but most of them will eventually return. Dynamics in the home are an important part of the environment of youth. Therefore, family life must be addressed in counseling. At a minimum, parents, and the other adults who live with children, need an orientation to The Seven Challenges Program, The Seven Challenges process, and the published Seven Challenges materials. During an orientation, parents learn about the stages of change, and the decision-making model of The Seven Challenges. It is essential they have realistic expectations of the program, and an understanding of the challenges process – i.e., counselors will work on building an honest relationship with youth that will allow for client self-disclosure; and youth will be taught various life skills while being guided through a decision making process that includes: thinking about their motivation for drug use, considering the needs they are trying to meet by using drugs, and examining the harm and potential from their drug use. This orientation allows parents to understand and recognize progress that their children make, and to acknowledge and reinforce it. Without this orientation, there is an enormous possibility of misunderstanding (For example: "The program approves of drug use by teens") and of working at cross-purposes (For example: Parental pressure creating the paradoxical effect of increasing a child's resistance to change).

FAMILY AND MULTI-FAMILY SERVICES

Beyond a basic orientation, family services and parent education have been successfully integrated in Seven Challenges programming.

In family and multi-family sessions, parents provide their perspective on the problems of their adolescent children and gain additional perspective from others. Parents support their children in overcoming drug and other problems, and in functioning better at home and outside the home. Parents also need to receive support and feedback for themselves. Together, parents and teens can address and confront family problems.

Most families need help in communication skills and in understanding one another's viewpoint better. They also usually need help in renegotiating power in the home:

> During adolescence, parents should extend increasing freedom to teens as they continue to mature.

However, this can only be done as youth demonstrate increasingly responsible behavior. Problems occur when youth behave irresponsibly in this process, or parents err, either in the direction of excessive permissiveness — which breeds indulgent and self-centered behavior — or in the direction of excessive authoritarianism, which breeds rebellion. I discuss this concept in great detail, elsewhere in my book *Saying NO is Not Enough*.[24]

With family services, each of the Challenges is an important springboard for discussion and increased understanding. Challenge One helps with increasing trust and a sense of safety in the home. In Challenge Two, parents get an understanding of why their children are using drugs – which needs are driving the use. In Challenge Three, parents and youth get an understanding of *each other's point of view* about the harm from drug use. Challenge Four can be especially meaningful because it is an opportunity to share responsibility for the problems that have occurred: a chance to consider how youth see themselves in the context of their family situation. Also in Challenge Four, family members can explore the connection between family problems and drug use. In Challenge Five, youth get more feedback on where their parents see them as headed. Finally, in Challenges Six and Seven, young people get support in making their decisions and following through with them.

PARENT EDUCATION

Parent education provides parents with help in managing family life with adolescents. This may include information about dealing with misbehavior, including drug use; establishing structure, with limits, boundaries, and rules; monitoring behavior; consistently maintaining the structure and enforcing rules; responding to misbehavior with education, counseling and, when indicated, sanctions; assuming a teaching and counseling role with adolescents; and renegotiating power arrangements in the family. Parents also need help with drug education, and with an understanding of how to respond to the drug use of their adolescents.

PARENT INVOLVEMENT

It is not always possible to involve parents in drug counseling for adolescents. Sometimes parents simply refuse to participate. Sometimes it is difficult to arrange because youth are in residential treatment far from their parents' homes, although counselors have managed in some settings to patch together sessions by using a speakerphone and a telephone connection.

Although many parents are eager to help in any way they can, with others it is a real challenge to engage their participation. Parents may resent being asked to participate or have anxieties of their own about participating in the process. Sometimes they are embarrassed or feel stigmatized about getting professional help. They may worry that they will be blamed for their children's problems. Sometimes they are concerned about exposure of their own shortcomings and problems. Ideally these obstacles to parent participation can be overcome.

Whenever possible counselors try to overcome obstacles to participation. However, under some circumstances it is not advisable to include parents in the treatment process. For example, parents should be excluded if they would do any of the following: take out their anger about involvement on their children; behave in excessively punitive ways with regard to what they hear in counseling; lie and hide the truth about issues to protect their self-image; or, punish youth who tell the truth and reveal family secrets in treatment. These tendencies and behaviors can be difficult to assess. Nevertheless, they require serious consideration because they can interfere and undermine successful treatment.

Many parents have their own serious problems, which may include problems with alcohol or other drugs. If these parents want, or would accept help, their participation could prove beneficial to their children. However when parents are resistant — and the problems intractable — it might be better to proceed without their participation.

Regardless of parent participation, most youth live at home or will return home. They need help in successful coping with the home environment. When parents have their own serious shortcomings, part of the help extended to youth may include assistance in how to cope with stressful or even oppressive conditions in the home. It also includes assistance in identifying other, caring adults in their environment to whom they can turn for support.

INTENSIVE OUTPATIENT PROGRAM

The Seven Challenges intensive outpatient program was included in an *independent evaluation* by the Center for Substance Abuse Treatment (CSAT), conducted by the University of Arizona. For those interested in replicating the program structure, or adapting it, the daily schedule of this effective IOP is described below. One unique feature of the program was that it included a Friday night recreational activity, which was planned by the youth. This proved important for teaching social skills, and for helping youth learn to have fun without drugs. The program lasted for eight weeks. It included four sessions per week. Upon completion of the initial program, youth were allowed to return once a week to a combined continuing care session and recreational activity (See FRIDAY, below) for up to four months.

TUESDAY: 3:30-6:30
Seven Challenges Discovery Group or Lifestyle Action Group
Seven Challenges Journaling
Life Skills Activity/Recreation/Art Therapy
Plan Friday Recreational Activity

WEDNESDAY: 6:30-9:00
Multi-family group
Parent Support Group
Seven Challenges Discovery Group and/or Journaling

THURSDAY: 3:30-6:30
Seven Challenges Discovery Group
Drug Free Education
Life Skills Activity/Coping Skills Activity
Seven Challenges Journaling

FRIDAY: 4:30-9:30
Brief Seven Challenges Discovery Group /or Lifestyle Action Group
Social Skills Training
Drug Free Lifestyle Recreational Activity

TIME REQUIRED TO COMPLETE THE PROGRAM

Program planners frequently inquire about how long it takes to complete The Seven Challenges Program. There is no simple answer because of individual differences among clients and differences in program intensity. Program intensity can vary from one or two outpatient sessions per week to intensive substance abuse residential treatment with significant time devoted to the program every day. There is also counselor variation, for example, in terms of how quickly they can review client journals and return them with feedback.

Nevertheless, it can be said that the intensive outpatient program, described above, surely provided ample time for most clients to complete the process during the intensive two-month process, with continuing care at the end. In juvenile correctional facilities the program often extends for eight or more months of work. In short term programs, counselors help clients move as far as they can through the process. Rather than rushing for completion of all journals, counselors strive for full completion of each journal that is used, and as much progress through the challenges as is possible. Sometimes counselors fall in the trap of trying to rush through the program because of limited lengths of stay. This can evolve into the mad rush for abstinence, which we know leads to compromised outcomes. It is better to lay a solid foundation for success than superficially strive to complete a task that requires more time. Also, counselors can "work on two levels" (see pages 115-125), when the need for abstinence is more immediate.

If clients do not complete the program before the length of stay expires, closure is important. Counselors should make sure that clients understand The Seven Challenges Process, know where the process leads, appreciate what they have accomplished so far, and know what remains to be accomplished. Clients can be encouraged to follow through, either on their own or with the help of other counselors. If aftercare is available, or professional help at another level of care, those providing the service can continue working with youth, reviewing past work, and starting from where the previous counseling left off.

TRAINING IN THE SEVEN CHALLENGES

In many respects The Seven Challenges Program is counter-intuitive. For example: The gut responses to adolescents who are abusing drugs is to try to convince them of the dangers, and to argue that they should quit. The approaches used in The Seven Challenges are not immediately obvious, even to seasoned and experienced clinicians. Training in this program is essential to maximize success. Training is also important because there is accumulated wisdom about the best ways of introducing and using Seven Challenges materials, and planning and structuring counseling sessions. Also there are specific clinical skills that are essential to success with The Seven Challenges. To protect the integrity and reputation of the program, The Seven Challenges® Training is required in order for individuals or agencies to announce that they are actually doing The Seven Challenges® Program. The type of required training and level of certification is an evolving process, which will be explained as it evolves at the website www.sevenchallenges.com.

Initial training focuses on the philosophy and principles of The Seven Challenges; use of Seven Challenges materials; state of the art Seven Challenges clinical skills for working with adolescent substance abuse; and program implementation issues. This is followed by additional training and support of Seven Challenges Leaders who will supervise, troubleshoot, and work for fidelity of implementation of the model at their agency.

In agencies providing The Seven Challenges Program, it is important that line staff, psych techs, youth workers, substance abuse workers, and other collateral staff members also receive initial training. Their training is not nearly as intensive as the training counselors receive, yet it should provide a clear introduction to the program and orient them to their role within the process. This is essential with The Seven Challenges because the program is counter-intuitive and, without this sort of intro- duction, line staff could easily work at cross-purposes from the counselors. Staff members spend much time interacting with youth, including sometimes in Seven Challenges groups, or other groups. Further, youth are required to ask adults they trust for feedback on certain issues in their *Seven Challenges Journals*. Without an ori- entation to the program, these formal and informal staff/client interactions could fly in the face of the counseling approaches used in Seven Challenges counseling sessions and the proclaimed philosophy of the program. We want the staff to be prepared to support youth with feedback in the most appropriate ways. (For example, by commu- nicating: "We are not trying to talk you into anything. We will not exaggerate the dangers of drugs. This is *your* decision. You need to think this through for yourself. This includes an honest consideration of the benefits of drugs, that is, the things you like about drugs.")

Staff members who do not understand and see the significance of the strategies would also be at risk of colluding with youth who might be looking for allies to undermine and criticize the counselors and the program methods. (Example: "This isn't a good program. The staff lets me talk about the good things about drugs. They don't even argue with me about how dangerous drugs are.")

Because The Seven Challenges publications have inherent value of their own, these materials are available to anyone who wishes to use them. Individuals can use the materials without certification in the program, but they cannot announce or claim to be doing The Seven Challenges Program® without training.

HOW TO USE
SEVEN CHALLENGES
MATERIALS

BOOKS, JOURNALS, AND POSTERS

INTRODUCING THE SEVEN CHALLENGES READINGS TO YOUTH

Many young people in drug treatment have had bad experiences and developed negative attitudes toward school and perhaps even toward reading. These attitudes are a barrier that must be surmounted in using a program with a powerful reading and writing component. To accomplish that, counselors must excite young people about the material — "selling" the program and materials. For this to happen, counselors themselves must know the material and be excited about it.

The Seven Challenges book should be introduced in a positive way, with considerable fanfare and enthusiasm, instead of simply giving it to youth. When finances allow, young people should be presented with the *gift* of *The Seven Challenges*. When finances are an issue, they can be presented as a *loan*. Here is a sample of one way of presenting the book in a positive manner, to minimize resistance and maximize open mindedness and interest.

> "I have here a book that we use in this program. I'd like to present it to you as a gift. The book is called *The Seven Challenges*. I think you're going to like the book because it doesn't lecture you about drugs, or exaggerate the dangers, or try to tell you how to live your life, or that you need to quit using drugs. It's a book that's written to help you think things through for yourself and make your own decisions about your life and your drug use. Only you can decide how to live your life. If you have already been doing this sort of thinking, then you will especially like this book because it will support you in something you are already doing."

Then you can open to page Roman numeral vi, point to the second paragraph, and say the following:

> "It says here that this book is based on the experiences of young people who managed to avoid serious drug problems or have been successful in overcoming drug problems. What these successful young people had in common was that they all challenged themselves and each other to think clearly about their lives and about their use of alcohol and other drugs. That's why the book is called *The Seven Challenges*."

Point to the third paragraph and continue:

> "Here it explains that the author says that he uses the word 'We' a lot in this book because the ideas are not his alone. They really come from the thoughts and experiences of the young people who have been successful. It is their insight. It is their thinking. He just wrote down their ideas."

Point to the fourth paragraph and read the first several sentences aloud. (This repeats what you already said, but is worthy of special emphasis.)

> "Here the author wrote: In this book no one tells you what to think or how to live your life. No one lectures you. No one exaggerates the dangers of drugs. Rather, this book is written to help you think things through *for yourself*. As you know,

you have to make your own decisions about alcohol and other drugs."

Next, from the second to last paragraph:

"The book is divided into seven chapters, one for each challenge. Let me tell you now a little bit about the challenges."

Open to the inside cover of *The Seven Challenges* – or point to a Seven Challenges poster – continue with the following:

"Here are The Seven Challenges."

Point to Challenge One.

"Challenge One is, 'We decided to talk openly and honestly about ourselves and about alcohol and other drugs.' This Challenge is about making it safe here so you can talk about what you really think and feel. We have to make it safe for you. You don't have to say you're going to quit using drugs in this program. You get to say what you really think and feel – whatever that is. To show that we are serious about this, take a look at Challenge Two."

Point to Challenge Two.

"Challenge Two is, 'We looked at what we liked about alcohol and other drugs, and why we were using them.' I think this Challenge shows that this program is serious about making it safe for you to talk about the truth. You get to talk about what you LIKE about drugs, without being cut short or censored. It's important to really understand yourself and know what you get from drugs."

Point to Challenge Three.

"Challenge Three is, 'We looked at our use of alcohol and other drugs to see if it had caused harm, or could cause harm.' There are no assumptions made that you have harmed yourself. This is a chance for you to think about it for yourself.

"After all, this is how people make decisions. You look at the good stuff about something, and the bad, and you decide what it is best for you. That's the way it works with The Seven Challenges. Look down here."

Point to Challenge Six.

"Challenge Six is, 'We made thoughtful decisions about our lives and about our use of alcohol and other drugs.' Notice that no one tells you to quit. This is probably the only program in the country for adolescents that doesn't say, 'We committed to being drug-free, or to abstinence.' This program really sticks to its principle, which is that: You decide. You have reached a time in life when you need to learn to think for yourself – to make your own wise choices. No one can, nor should, be making these choices for you.

"So here, let me give you the book. Why don't you take it back with you? Touch it. Feel it. Hold it. Take a peek at it. See you what think. (Pause) I think you'll like it."

Avoid giving assignments when first presenting the book. The idea is just to let a young person get comfortable with it. Of course, if the young person has difficulties in reading, counselors should read some portions of the book to the youth and explain that he or she will be getting help with the reading from a staff person, or possibly from another young person who would serve as a reader. All youth should be screened for their reading ability upon entry in the program to identify those who will need extra assistance in using the materials. It is important to save youth from embarrassment. All written materials in the program are presented in very elementary ways, with simple, easy to read language. Nevertheless, some youth will struggle and need help. In extreme cases, the whole program will have to be presented orally. (More on this under Reading Problems, on page 100.)

HOW ARE THE READINGS USED?

There is no single way to use The Seven Challenges readings. The book has been used in many different ways. Sometimes group leaders ask young people to select a reading of their choice to begin group sessions, perhaps after a check-in period. A short discussion can follow, leading with questions such as: "What do you think? Does any of this apply to you? Do you know people who have had experiences like these?" Individual sessions can also begin with a reading. Often, counselors select relevant readings and integrate them as part of an activity during a group, individual, or family session. Also, readings can be brought to bear upon discussions when youth are engaged in problem-solving work. *Counselors should be fully familiar with the material — know it well and be able to draw upon it as a resource to address specific issues as a discussion evolves in an individual, group, or family session.*

Before completing written work in a journal, it is expected that young people will finish reading the corresponding chapter in *The Seven Challenges* book. They may have to do this on their own, or during structured journaling sessions in which they either read from the book or write in their journals. Counselors should not sign off on a journal until it is clear that the client has read the corresponding chapter on that particular challenge in *The Seven Challenges*. The readings are important in thinking through the issues.

INTRODUCING THE SEVEN CHALLENGES JOURNALS TO YOUTH

BASIC JOURNAL INFORMATION

Journals are a special, personal, and powerful way to help young people in several ways: to think about their lives and their use of alcohol and other drugs; to contemplate, decide, and prepare to make changes; and to successfully implement the desired changes. Young people will often express thoughts and feelings in writing that they would not say in person. Writing provides an opportunity for reflection, in contrast to the immediate response expected in face-to-face communication. The absence of an immediate audience also allows some freedom in expressing oneself. These are reasons why the *Seven Challenges Journals* are important tools in this program.

The Journals use a question and answer format and look like workbooks. However they are called journals, in part, to be more "kid friendly," by avoiding labels that may remind youth of unhappy experiences in school with workbooks and other written work. So we have chosen to call these resources journals, rather than workbooks, and prefer to refer to the effort required as writing, rather than work. We ask youth to "Write in your journals" rather than "Work in your workbooks."

Also, we call the publications journals because the writing is very personal, much like writing in one's own personal journal. The publications could most accurately be defined as "interactive journals" because staff members respond supportively to what youth write, in order to promote a back and forth dialogue. Journals are a good way for young people to express themselves and get constructive feedback from an adult who cares. The free expression and supportive responses help them in making their own informed decisions about their lives and their use of alcohol and other drugs.

There are a total of nine journals in the program. Challenges Two, Three, Four, Five and Six each has one. Challenges One and Seven each has two. Challenge One has two journals — Part One and Part Two. *Challenge One, Part One* is about trust — and talking openly and honestly about one's life and drug use. *Challenge One, Part Two* is for writing a drug history. (In most clinical work, drug histories are taken upon admission. It is interesting to take another drug history somewhat later, after working to create a climate of honesty. Also, initial drug histories are often taken orally. *Challenge One, Part Two*, is a written follow up.)

Challenge Seven also has two parts. It is preceded by Challenge Six in which young people are asked to make decisions about (a) personal changes and lifestyle issues and (b) their use of alcohol and other drugs. *Challenge Seven, Part One*, follows through on the decisions about personal changes and lifestyle issues. *Challenge Seven, Part Two*, follows through on relapse prevention and the drug decisions.

The way the process works is that clients write in the journals. Counselors carefully read the journals; respond with extensive, supportive feedback and questions in the margins; and then return them to the youth. Journals go back and forth between clients and counselors several times, with a written dialogue evolving on the various pages. This becomes a special type of communication, as young people begin to recognize that someone is really paying attention to them and what they have to say; that counselors are making the effort of responding; and are responding in a positive way. (There are important guidelines, discussed below, about how to respond to the journals to increase productive responses and reduce defensiveness.) Ideally, the same person comments in the journals all through the program, so that a strong journaling alliance is developed. It becomes a special relationship.

If counselors do not invest the time to read the journals carefully and to respond extensively, clients are likely to trivialize the importance of this resource and treat it as another hoop through which they must jump.

In most programs, structured time is set aside for young people to read and write in their journals. Ideally some of that time would be in a group, with adults present to supervise. The group setting gives youth an opportunity to get help from staff in their writing, and to get the feedback from peers and adults that is required in order to respond to some of the questions in the journals. Highly motivated young people will also find their own time to write in their journals.

Youth are given one journal at a time. They do not receive the next journal in the series until the counselor signs off on the current one. This happens when counselors conclude that the effort is thorough, the work is complete, and full benefits have been derived from the dialogue. After each journal is completed, counselors meet with the youth to discuss what was learned from the effort doing this journal. At the end of this meeting, counselors present the client with the Seven Challenges' Diploma that corresponds to that journal. (See Diplomas, discussed on pages 113-114.) Each diploma is designed to reinforce the work of that challenge. Some counselors also require clients to write a brief statement about what they have learned from each challenge, and perhaps to share it in a group session. Finally, in group sssions youth are recognized for the completion of each journal.

MODEL STATEMENT FOR HANDING OUT JOURNALS

Journals that require writing and effort probably will not, at first, be viewed in a positive light by young people who may have had negative experiences in school and with expressing themselves in writing. As with the readings, a special effort is required to get young people involved in the use of the journals.

The Journals should be introduced in a positive manner to inspire interest and excitement about the process. Below is a model statement of such a presentation.

> "This program has nine journals that will be given to you, one at a time. I think you'll like these journals because they are an opportunity to do some more thinking about your life and about your use of alcohol and other drugs. Writing in a journal is a special way to think about your own life. This is how it works. You write in your journal and when you finish, you pass it along to me. I'll read it and write comments in the margins – they'll always be supportive — and I'll ask some questions. We'll end up having this very special written dialogue. The journal will pass back and forth between us several times until the work is complete. I think you'll see that this gives us a whole other way to communicate with each other. All in all, we'll have our group sessions, our one-to-one sessions, and our communication through writing.

> "Journaling requires effort. But I think, once we get going, you'll like it and feel that the payoffs are worth the effort. So, here's the first journal. Why don't you take a look and see what you think.

> "I think these journals are very valuable. I'll put in a lot of effort in carefully reading what you write and responding to you. I really want to understand your point

of view and make this program work for you. I do expect that you'll also make an effort, on your end, so that you can get the most out of the journals.

"You'll see, too, that this is not like schoolwork. First, there are no grades; no wrong answers. With journaling, you write your own thoughts and feelings. I won't be making corrections or anything of the sort in your journals. Rather, you share your point of view and I'll share mine.

"Also, the journals are *not* meant to be hoops that you rush through in order to get finished. Please take your time and think about the questions. Think about what you write. You'll get more out of this process if you do that.

"Finally, I want to be very clear. The journals ALWAYS go back and forth several times. When I return them to you, it does NOT mean you have failed in any way. It means that we have begun the dialogue and now will continue with it."

WHO SEES THE JOURNALS?

In introducing the journals, it is wise to include a discussion of who sees the journals and who keeps them in the end. This is handled differently in different situations. It is highly recommended that the journals only go between the counselor and the client. Opening them to other staff or to other youth tends to inhibit what is written. In one agency, counselors tried using journal responses as the basis for group discussion, with young people having the option of *not* sharing on any particular day. Even though clients were told they could opt out of a discussion whenever they wanted, it was still clear that they were significantly censoring what they were writing in their journals. Somehow they were inhibited by the thought of the group discussions about journal content. Experience has also shown that young people are more willing to self disclose when they know that only one staff will be responding to their journals. Therefore the conclusion: The smaller the audience, the better; the larger the audience, the greater the amount of self-censorship.

Parents also should not see the journals. This would surely inhibit honest expression by youth.

Occasionally, youth may write something in the journals that counselors feel would be good to discuss in a group setting. On these occasions counselors can ask, "Would you be willing to share this with the group? You might get some helpful feedback." As long as this practice is kept to a minimum, it can be very effective in generating important discussions of important issues.

Ideally, clients should keep their journals when they complete the program, just as they would keep their own personal journal. Completed journals can be passed along from counselor to counselor for aftercare, or continuing care.

OVERCOMING RESISTANCE TO JOURNALS: BUILDING INTEREST, EXCITEMENT AND INVOLVEMENT IN THE JOURNALING PROCESS

Some youth immediately embrace the use of the journals. Others see them as more work, almost like schoolwork, and another hoop through which they must jump. They may have negative feelings about workbooks and expect that they'll receive negative evaluations of their work. When the journals are seen as another hoop, young people generally rush through the first one – giving superficial answers and trying to "get it over with." This is where artful feedback is so important. Instead of criticizing youth who may be doing superficial work, counselors take a positive and expansive approach. We ask clients to tell us more, and to complete unanswered portions of the journals. We pepper responses with positive acknowledgement for what has been presented. We show that we are paying attention to what is written – and not doing as they might expect, either marking everything wrong (making negative judgments) or simply treating the journals as unimportant (by accepting superficial work and merrily proceeding along).

Many young people in drug treatment programs are hungry for adult attention. The journals are an excellent way to show interest in them and in what they think and feel. They will see that someone cares enough to carefully read what is written, and to try to understand them. They will see many positive and encouraging responses to what they write. This spawns a special, supportive relationship. When young people are accepted in this way, they are receptive to the work and will write more in their journals. Gradually clients accept the requirements, give longer and more complete responses, and begin to value the journals.

To summarize: Counselors help youth move from superficiality to greater depth in their journal writing by (1) showing that they pay attention; (2) responding in positive, supportive and expansive ways; and (3) being clear that the writing must be completed in a satisfactory way in order to move through the program.

Some clients bitterly oppose the books and journals – calling them stupid, or saying "I know all this stuff," or finding one reason or another to put down the materials. Counselors counter by confidently explaining that the program is really an excellent one, and that they (the youth) should give it a try. Counselors say that they have seen its effectiveness over and over again (or, if they are new to The Seven Challenges, that they know it is effective in helping young people). Once the client's discontent has been expressed and acknowledged, counselors must not allow continued repetition of complaints. They may, in the end, have to say, "Sorry, this is your work; you need to do it," and then: "I know you don't like it. I hope that as you do begin to use these journals you will see their value and begin to like them more." But counselors should avoid falling in the trap of wasting precious counseling time debating the merits of the program. The idea of standing firm without getting into an endless debate, or engaging in a power struggle, is not a clinical skill unique to The Seven Challenges. It involves the fine art of allowing for discontent, avoiding complaint sessions and staying on message: "You need to do your work. This is your work in this program."

Another reason that youth sometimes resist drug treatment is because of fear of: (1) what they might learn about themselves, and (2) the possibility of deciding to quit using drugs. To counteract these fears counselors add: "Look, sometimes people complain about the program because they are afraid of what they might uncover or reveal about themselves, or where this all might lead. I don't know if this is true for you, but you do need to start writing in these journals. That's required in this program. I can assure you, however, that we will support you. Sometimes it's hard for people to look at themselves and their lives. But, we will help you."

READING PROBLEMS

In a program with strong reading and writing materials, it is essential that counselors make an assessment of a youth's verbal abilities before handing out books and journals. It is important not to embarrass young people about their inability to read or write, or other verbal shortcomings. If young people cannot read, then someone should read the material to them, and assist them with the writing.

To avoid embarrassment, clients are not asked to read out loud unless it is known that they can read. Unless it is clear that everyone in a group can read comfortably, counselors do not follow the practice of going around the circle and having each person take a turn reading. Rather, volunteers are asked to read.

The Seven Challenges materials should never become a barrier to success in the program. When counselors hand out materials, they should be clear: "Tell me if you have any problem with reading or writing. I'll help you or I'll get you help." Even more specifically, counselors should say, "If there are any sentences or questions that you don't understand, tell me and I will help you with them." Counselors may need to sit with individuals to help them, or even walk them through the materials. On occasions, counselors help youth muddle their way through the books and journals, on a sentence by sentence basis. Sometimes more advanced peers are asked to help with the reading, unless the youth who needs help is uncomfortable with this arrangement.

Questions have been asked: Can non-readers do the program? Can a modified version of the program be done without the materials? In a sense, the answer is yes. The essence of the program involves using The Seven Challenges process to help young people make wise decisions about their lives. The published materials are simply tools to help with the process. However, the books and journals are enormously powerful tools. An important resource is lost if the materials are not used.

REVIEWING AND RESPONDING TO JOURNALS

RESPONDING TO JOURNALS

Seven Challenges Journals were written to provide a tool whereby young people could take a look at their own lives – thoughts, feelings behavior, and experiences — and think through their options and choices. The Journals are interactive, with counselors participating in a written dialogue with youth. Counselors provide assistance in eliciting expression from young people, and in expanding, clarifying and enriching the thought processes. Counselors offer support and empathy. They add insight to the process.

In responding to journals, counselors should communicate a tone of caring, interest, empathy, support, and curiosity. They should encourage and reinforce effort, honesty and open expression of thoughts and feelings. Comments should be expansive, as in, "I'm curious, please tell me more." Counselors should provide abundant and supportive responses on each and every page.

Counselors should *not* see the job as correcting journals. Rather they are responding to youth and creating a dialogue. Red ink should be avoided. The tone of comments should not be preachy, disapproving, harshly critical, harshly confrontational, or argumentative. Beware of a tendency to try to convince youth that drugs are dangerous, or that they must quit using drugs. This tendency is especially likely to occur in response to Challenge Two when clients are asked about what they "like about drugs."

In responding to journals, counselors set high standards and expectations by insisting that all work is complete and comprehensive. When pages are incomplete, they *politely request the completion of the work.* For example:

- You left out this question. Please complete it.

- You only listed three reasons. Please fill in *all* blank spaces.

- Please add some more reasons to your list.

- Please complete this page.

Sometimes what youth write in journals will not be clear. Counselors should *request clarification*, as below:

- I don't quite follow this. Could you please explain what you mean by___?

- I don't know this drug you mentioned. Could you tell me more about it?

- I don't quite understand. Can you tell me why this happened?

Many counselor responses to youth will be in the form of questions. This is part of establishing the dialogue. It is best to ask questions in a way that could be described as a neutral probe. It is neutral in the sense of not trying to prove a point or push an agenda. Rather, questions are asked in the spirit of gaining greater understanding.

There are two major categories of responses to the journals. One category consists of *emotional and relationship comments* – showing you care, showing your interest and curiosity, expressing empathy, communicating acceptance, and providing support.

The other major category consists of *cognitive/intellectual comments* — making observations or generalizations, making connections between different thoughts and different responses in the journals, pointing out apparent contradictions, exploring discrepancies, trying to clarify contradictions, teaching, and sensitively offering interpretations.

WRITING EMOTIONAL/RELATIONSHIP COMMENTS IN JOURNALS

Some of the emotional/relationship comments fall in the following sub-categories:

Curious and Expansive

This is interesting. Please tell me more.

How did you feel?

What were you thinking at the time?

What else happened?

Why do you think this has happened?

Is it worth it?

Which is more important to you now?

Empathy and Validation

That must have hurt.

You must have felt _____.

I can see why you would feel this way.

Caring

I hope things work out for you.

It makes me sad to hear that this happened to you.

You really do deserve something better than that.

I'm with you all the way on this.

Praise

Very good.

Good.

Great work.

It's good you can be so honest about this.

It sounds like you were really thinking clearly.

You seem to be willing to recognize your mistakes. That's great.

That was really nice of you to do this.

Encouragement

> This is terrific. Keep up your effort.
>
> You are really working hard on this.
>
> Your willingness to be honest here will help you later.

WRITING COGNITIVE/INTELLECTUAL COMMENTS IN JOURNALS

Other comments in journals are more cognitive/intellectual in nature. Here are some specific guidelines and recommendations with regard to this type of feedback.

- Avoid self-certainty: State opinions as opinions, not facts. Examples: "In my opinion..."; "I think...."

- State conjectures as conjectures, not fact. Examples: "It seems to me..."; "Maybe this means....."; "I wonder if...."

- Explain your own thinking about a point of view so that clients understand the underlying reasons for your conclusions.

- Leave open the possibility that there might be other ways to look at issues, or other opinions, besides the way you see them.

- Show interest in what the client thinks by requesting his or her point of view. Examples: "What do you think?"; "How do you see things?"; "Do you think this is possible?"; "What's your opinion?"

- Do not use journals to argue or try to prove a point. Use them for a lively dialogue.

- Teach, when possible, but without getting preachy.

For more information on this topic, you can consult another publication of mine, *Who's on Top; Who's on Bottom: How Couples Can Learn to Share Power.* It provides great detail about the risks of closing off dialogue with self-certainty, the necessity of leaving room for opposing opinions, and strategies for communicating cooperatively.[25] Although the context of that discourse is another topic – couple's relationships – the principles and practices are highly applicable in this program.

Typical journal comments of the more cognitive nature might fall in the following sub-categories and sound like these:

Observations / Generalizations

> It seems as though it is important to you to be liked.
>
> It seems like you feel safest opening up to people who have had similar experiences as your own.
>
> It seems that you have often used drugs when you were angry and wanted to calm down.

Giving Opinions / Thoughtful Comments

You said you had 20 blackouts from drinking. That sounds like a lot to me. What do you think?

I think it's a bad idea to get high when you meet new people. They won't see the real you – and you don't learn how to cope with meeting people. What do you think?

In my opinion that's a lot of cocaine you have been using? What do you think?

Interpretations

Interpretations are a special type of opinion or conjecture, usually based on considerable observation. They are tentative attempts to find underlying psychological motivations for behavior. They can be helpful in stimulating clients' reflections. They can also be a volatile, highly charged form of communication. Counselors should make interpretations with care to avoid sounding as though they *know* something with certainty about which they are only speculating, and to avoid sounding as though they have a corner on the truth.

It sounds as though you might be afraid of this. Is that a possibility?

Maybe you used drugs when you were feeling bad about yourself? What do you think?

If counselors sound too self-certain, clients will think, or say: "Don't go telling me what I'm thinking (or doing)."

Teaching

Did you know that this (doing drugs you said you never would do, and doing more drugs than you planned on doing) often signifies a drug problem?

One of the ways that people cope with stress is by learning relaxation skills. Would this interest you?

These drugs you just mentioned are called inhalants. Did you know they are particularly dangerous? Let's talk about this.

Making Connections

Client self-understanding can be enhanced by making connections between what they write in different sections of their journals, or between what they say in face-to-face meetings and what they write in journals. Counselors can connect thoughts that clients may not have connected in their own minds. Comments of this sort can be especially powerful because they show that counselors are really paying attention.

You said... on page.... Now you are saying.... Do you think there is a connection between them?

Example: "You said you could talk with your sister because she has been through the same stuff. You also said she is someone you really trust. Do you think maybe this is part of why you trust her so much?"

Another example: "You talked about all the anger you have. Do you think the things you are writing here about your Dad might be connected to the anger?"

Clarifying Contradictions

Clients sometimes express different viewpoints at different times that appear to contradict one another. There may be contradictions between what is written in different sections of a journal, or between what is written and what is spoken in face-to-face communication. Exploring these contradictions can increase client self-understanding. In the spirit of Seven Challenges journaling, the goal is not to expose the contradictions, or "catch" clients making contradictions. Rather the goal is to help clarify differing points of view and consider what the contradictions represent. For example, sometimes people will say positive things about a parent in a group because of embarrassment about the reality, but then honestly report their true negative feelings in a journal. Sometimes, the opposite occurs. They express their true feelings in a group session, but put wishful thinking in their journal. In either case, counselors explore contradictions in a supportive and inquisitive way. For example:

In our group, I think you said that you have never gotten in trouble with the law when using drugs. But it sounds like you were using drugs this time when you did get in trouble. Weren't you high when this happened? What do you think about this? Which one, do you think, is what really happened?

Sometimes contradictions reflect client ambivalence. People may have two opposing thoughts or feelings and go back and forth between them. Counselors can help clients identify, clarify, and sometimes even resolve their ambivalence.

Supportively Pointing Out Discrepancy

Sometimes a contradiction is evident between a stated goal and actual behavior; or a stated value and actual behavior. For example, there may be a discrepancy between what a person wants to achieve (a career as a veterinarian) and their behavior (not going to school); or between something they say is an important value (for example, honesty) and their behavior (for example, lying). In the spirit of journaling, these contradictions can be noted and explored in a supportive and caring tone. For example:

You say you want to be a veterinarian when you grow up. But you haven't been attending classes in high school. I am puzzled about how you will achieve what you want to achieve unless you do something about this. What do you think?

Miller has written with great clarity about the strategy of pointing out discrepancy in his book, *Motivational Interviewing*.[26]

Raise Thought Provoking Questions (but avoid confrontation)

These are questions that push young people to think further about an issue. For example, one girl seemed to be overly self-critical and perhaps misinformed. In her summary at the end of *Journal One, Part One*, she indicated that as a result of her effort in her journal: "I realized that I'm an addict." The comment from her counselor was: "Are you sure? Why do you say you are an addict? It sounds more like drug abuse then addiction to me."

Below are other examples of thought provoking questions:

Could this possibly be related to your problems with drugs?

Does this possibly explain your anger?

You said that 'being honest with yourself' is important for making a better life. Now you are saying that you can get hurt if you are "honest with yourself." Do you think it is worth the risk? Please tell me where you stand.

Many people gave you feedback that you are abusing drugs. You seem to disagree. Why do you think they say you are harmfully involved with drugs?

Caring Confrontation

Feedback in the journals evolves as the relationship between counselor and client evolves. At first, there is more emphasis on encouragement and relationship building, and little that might arouse defenses, and little in the way of interpretations. The primary goal is to create a climate of honesty and self-disclosure. As the relationship evolves and youth are more committed to the process and connected to their counselors, it is increasingly possible to ask some tougher, more challenging questions.

Caring confrontation in counseling sessions is discussed on pages 56-57 of this publication. Similarly, caring confrontation can be incorporated in responding to journals.

When you talk about showing your anger in these ways, I worry that you might hurt someone else or hurt yourself.

I think what you just said about using drugs in this way is dangerous. I worry for your safety.

I think this idea of yours is reckless. That's my opinion. What do you think?

SPECIAL CONCERNS REQUIRING FACE-TO-FACE FOLLOW UP

Sometimes counselors will choose to supplement written comments with face-to-face discussions. This occurs when something profoundly important or potentially dangerous is noted, and counselors want to make sure that their communication with a client is clear and thorough. Also, counselors sometimes need to make lengthy responses, and there is not enough time, or space on the page, to respond adequately in writing. So, counselors add to their written response:

"Let's talk about this."

Then counselors must be sure to follow up with face-to-face discussion. Here are some more examples:

You must be very upset. Let's talk about this.

Did you know this can be dangerous? Let's talk about it.

I want to explain something about this. Let's talk.

CONCERNS ABOUT DEFACING THE JOURNALS

Because journals are usually very personal possessions, some counselors have been reluctant to write in the margins, concerned that they would be defacing a child's personal belongings. Instead of responding in writing, they responded with direct, spoken communication. The problem with this is that the journals are designed to be a supplement to spoken communication. When communication becomes spoken, the special impact of written communications is diminished. Another problem is that youth do not have a written record of the dialogue, which shows the evolution of their thinking. This, too, is a loss. Some counselors tried responding with "post it" notes so their comments could be removed. However, removing the counselors' comments leaves only the youth's responses and no record of the dialogue. *The journal is intended to be an interactive experience, and to include counselor comments.* Contrary to what some counselors have feared – their writing is not seen as an intrusion. Rather, youth are almost always pleased to see the positive feedback in their journals.

MOVING THROUGH THE PROGRAM

The journals are designed to be used by youth at their own individual pace. Initially it was thought that the message should be, "Do the work well and pace doesn't matter." Over time, it has become clear that some element of incentive can improve productivity. For example, counselors may require that clients complete certain journals in order to advance in a level system. This can serve as an incentive to work harder and faster. However, too much pressure or too heavy an emphasis on such incentives will compromise the quality of work. So it is wise to consider balancing the need for quality and the desire to motivate speed and effort. Under no circumstances should writing in the journals be rushed.

In some agencies, the journals have been used in a more regimented fashion, sort of one-size-fits-all. For example, in one agency the goal was established that one journal would be completed each week. It was a nine-week length of stay, and the idea was to finish a journal per week, and all journals by the end of the sessions. In another agency, all youth were asked to complete the same pages together during a certain time frame. The Seven Challenges Program does not prescribe how and when to move through the materials. However, the idea of rushing youth or assuming they would all move at the same pace is contrary to the intent of the program. The goal should not be to complete the journals, as desirable as that might be. Rather, the goal should be to advance youth as far as they can profitably go in the process in the time that is available. Also, when all clients start and move through the program at the same time and same pace, much is lost in terms of group process. (See Group Composition on pages 77-78.) Unfortunately, administrative necessity in terms of program organization sometimes takes precedence over the ideal clinical approach to the work.

When an agency's length of stay does not allow completion of the entire The Seven Challenges Program, it would be senseless to rush youth through the journals. The whole idea of the program is that superficial work does not really benefit clients. It makes much better sense to take young people as far as they will go in the change process. (See Group Composition onp pages 77-78.) If youth only complete some of the journals, counselors can help them think about what they have accomplished, what lies ahead in their decision making, and how they will follow up, either on their own or with other counselors.

FREQUENTLY ASKED QUESTIONS ABOUT THE JOURNALING PROCESS

What about insincere and superficial responses?

These responses should be anticipated or even expected at the beginning. Some young people think that they can breeze through with superficiality. Others, with a "so what" attitude, expect to receive negative feedback as they "go through the hoops." As stated earlier, these attitudes can usually be reversed by counselors showing interest in their clients' work and point of view; providing abundant positive and supportive responses; and showing that superficiality will not lead to progress through, and completion of, the program. Generally, clients respond to this by working harder and being more serious in their efforts. In any event, counselors need to pay attention to determine whether clients are taking the work to heart, and honestly and fully answering questions in the journals. If doubts linger, counselors should trust their intuition and raise the issue. This can be done skillfully, without making accusations. Counselors can say, "This just doesn't sound like you" or "This is not like what you have been saying in group" or "This doesn't really match the information I have about you." Sometimes a humorous, "Oh c'mon, what's really going on" can be effective.

If efforts remain superficial, counselors do not move on to the next journal. Instead they discuss the superficiality with the youth. We do not tell young people that they must quit using drugs. However, we do tell them that a requirement of the program is that they honestly look at their lives by doing the required work. The message is: "You can't fake your way through this program, or breeze your way through it. You must do the work." Eventually they will do it.

Can we have the youth respond to just a few pages and pass the journal back to us for feedback – a little at a time?

This has been tried in some settings. However, there is a certain loss of flow that goes with it. Counselors find it harder to keep track of what has been written, and where they stand on the dialogue with clients. (Remember that the journals pass back and forth several times. If the journals are reviewed in a piecemeal way, it is hard to remember where each "conversation thread" was left.) It is easier to keep track of the dialogue when the whole book is reviewed at once. The journals are most effective when youth complete all pages before handing them in.

When do you sign off on a journal and move on to the next?

Counselors sign off on journals when all questions are answered, the written dialogue has taken place, and the work is complete and substantial. Another requirement is that the corresponding chapter has been read in *The Seven Challenges* book.

Although counselors should use written communication for feedback and dialogue as youth are working on their journals, when the process for each journal is finally complete, a face-to-face meeting is recommended. In this meeting youth will discuss what they have learned from the particular journal. Then they are presented with the diploma for that journal.

What if someone seems to be rushing through the journals?

Some verbally fluent and ambitious youth try to rush through the journals. It is important to slow them down. The purpose of the program is to provide an opportunity for young people to be introspective and think about their lives. When clients are rushing, counselors slow down the process by expanding the discussion and giving enriching exercises. Counselors are frank that they are slowing things down – that they want youth to really reflect on the material that is covered in the journals.

Who holds the books between sessions?

In the best of all worlds, young people would retain the books and journals between sessions. This would give them a chance to read and write when they felt like it. Hopefully, the materials would become a part of their lives. However, there is a serious problem of young people losing, misplacing or forgetting their books and journals. This is especially true in outpatient settings. Even in residential settings, it is easier to keep track of materials if staff holds them. Privacy is another issue. Clients are more vulnerable to invasion of privacy if they bring the materials home or have them in their rooms in a residential setting. In outpatient programs, the staff generally holds the journals between sessions, except under special circumstances, or with especially motivated clients. *The Seven Challenges* book is taken home for reading more often than the journals. Clearly if staff holds the books and journals, ample access must be provided to youth during scheduled program time. In some residential settings, youth maintain possession of their books and journals. In others, staff holds them so they do not get lost.

What about oral responses to the journaling of youth?

Face-to-face discussion is not a good substitute for written responses to journals. The idea of written communication is to stimulate another level of communication, to supplement what is occurring in normal discussion. People will write in journals information they would not necessarily express in face-to-face communication. This benefit is lost when counselors respond to journals in special meetings or counseling sessions.

When the staff writes responses in the journal, there is clear evidence of the interest, effort, and commitment of the counselor. This evidence tends to inspire more youth effort and commitment. (When staff are hard-pressed for time and choose to respond in meetings, youth sense that counselors are taking a shortcut and do not value this endeavor. Consequently, they will tend to treat the journals as a meaningless formality.)

The written exchange provides a record of the dialogue between youth and counselor. This is important if a counselor were to leave before the client completes treatment. It is also important for the use of aftercare professionals who would want to continue the dialogue.

(In a related matter: To maintain a written record of the exchange, clients are asked *not* to erase their own previous remarks as they respond to counselor comments in the journal. The point is made that it is important to show the dialogue that has occurred - the record of the exchange.)

It is only after the written dialogue is complete in each journal that face-to-face discussion is advisable for closure. At this meeting, the diploma is awarded.

What about youth with low intellect?

Whether individuals have high or low intellect, the bottom line is that they will be making their own decisions about drug use, and should be sharpening their thinking skills. It could be argued that youth with low intellect would especially need a program such as this. It provides them with an added experience with supervision in learning to think through their decisions for themselves.

What about people who are not especially introspective?

This program will feel quite alien to them at first. Counselors need to work with them to gain acceptance of this model. The selling point is: "You have to make your own decisions in life. In order to make good decisions, including decisions about things that are as powerful as drugs, you really need to take a careful look at yourself and your life. Although you have not tended to be introspective, this is a skill that it important to learn." Counselors can teach people both the value of introspection and the art of good decision-making.

What about youth who received counseling in one place and then moved to another, for continuing care or aftercare?

We do not want program participants to feel as though the journals are simply obstacles to overcome. We do not want to create resentment. For this reason, we would not ask them to completely start at the beginning and do the work over again in journals. The new counselor could ask the clients where they left off. They could discuss the need to learn about what the youth has done so far. If either the counselors or youth have possession of the journals, counselors could suggest that because of time passing and a change of setting, maybe youth would want to revise some of what they wrote before. Youth can be asked to review the journals and make any changes they wish using a different color ink (or pencil). Then, the new counselor can review the journal. If the journals are not available, youth can be asked to summarize their work with each completed challenge. On the basis of the summary, youth might be asked to repeat some of the work that was previously done in journals – not in a punitive sense, but "so I can fully understand your thinking" and so "we can have our own dialogue about some of the issues."

DIPLOMAS

One guiding principle of The Seven Challenges Program is that success is recognized and reinforced in smaller increments (see pages 46-48).

Diplomas are designed to reinforce effort and success in completing journals, and to reinforce the essential messages of each challenge. Below are the statements that appear on diplomas for each of the journals.

> Congratulations on completing the *Challenge One Journal, Part One*. You have successfully made a strong effort to open up, talk honestly, and build trust. Trust is important. Good relationships make a difference. We hope you will trust us and feel a lot of support in this program as you think about your life and make your own decisions.

> Congratulations on completing the *Challenge One Journal, Part Two*. You have successfully put your drug history in writing, which will give you a chance to take a careful look at it with open eyes. It will help you make your own wise decisions and a good future for yourself.

> Congratulations on completing the *Challenge Two Journal*. You have begun to have a deeper understanding of what you like about alcohol and other drugs and why you use them. This is important information when you make decisions about drug use in the future. We hope we can help you find many new ways to find pleasure and have a good life.

> Congratulations on completing the *Challenge Three Journal*. You have begun to build a deeper understanding of how you have been harmed by alcohol or other drugs, or could be harmed by them. We hope you can find ways to move forward and prevent future harm.

> Congratulations on completing the *Challenge Four Journal*. You have successfully considered how your situation and other people have affected you. You have considered your own responsibility for resolving your problems. We hope you are ready to take control of your future and use your personal strength to make good things happen.

> Congratulations on completing the *Challenge Five Journal*. You have successfully thought about your direction in life and your future. This will help you control where you are headed. We wish you much wisdom, happiness, and strength as you move forward.

> Congratulations on completing the *Challenge Six Journal*. You have successfully made your own decisions. You can take control of your own life.

Congratulations on completing the *Challenge Seven Journal, Part One*. You have made big strides in implementing changes in your life and lifestyle. We hope you will remain strong, continue to grow, make progress, and learn from any and all mistakes or setbacks.

Congratulations on completing the *Challenge Seven Journal, Part Two*. You have made big strides in overcoming alcohol and other drug problems. We wish you much success and happiness as you free yourself from the harmful effects of alcohol and other drugs, and make a good life for yourself – on your own terms.

WORKING ON TWO LEVELS

WHEN THE COURTS,

COMMUNITY, JUVENILE CORRECTIONS,

OR SCHOOLS REQUIRE

IMMEDIATE ABSTINENCE

REQUIRING ABSTINENCE / READINESS FOR ABSTINENCE

Many adolescents receive drug treatment services that are mandated by schools, courts, or the juvenile justice system. These institutions may *require clients to quit using drugs*, either for eligibility for a special program, such as drug court; or as a condition of probation; or in anticipation of parole (or probation) upon release from a juvenile correctional setting; or as a condition of avoiding suspension from school.

Of course we wish all young people in treatment would immediately quit abusing drugs because so much harm could be prevented. However, we know that only a very small percentage of the adolescent population that presents for drug treatment services are ready to make informed, internally motivated, and committed decisions to quit using...and are prepared to succeed. Another tiny percentage of youth are on the cusp of readiness to quit and can be thrust into action by court insistence, or the insistence of other authorities, that they maintain abstinence in order to qualify for a special program. For these youth, insistence upon immediate abstinence is a perfect match. We should do our best to identify these individuals and set the bar high. To do less would be to underestimate them. However, working only with these youth, and not others, would be to cast a very small net. Surely 95%, or more, of drug abusing youth mandated to treatment do not fit in the above categories. What about the other youth – the vast majority — who are far from ready, willing, and able to quit? As noted earlier, we know that we must avoid the mad rush for abstinence in drug counseling with youth because it does not work. We should meet young people at their actual starting point, not where we wish they were starting.

As stated earlier in this manual, most youth with drug problems enter treatment in the earlier stages of change.

- They may not recognize that they have a problem, perhaps because they live in families or communities where drug use is almost universal, or perhaps because of psychological reasons, unique to themselves.

- They may see a problem, but not be aware of any way to resolve it.

- They may see a problem and a way to resolve it, but feel overwhelmed by the thought of what their lives would be like if they did not have drugs as a crutch. (Here are a few examples: Young clients may be clinically *depressed*, perhaps even suicidal, and have so much distress that they do not feel they could cope without drugs; young clients may experience so much *anxiety* in their daily lives that they do not feel they could make it through the day without drugs; young clients may *suffer such pain* from abuse, or other trauma, that they do not feel they could cope with life without drugs.)

- They may want to make changes, but feel immobilized by fear of failure. They do not believe they could succeed with abstinence. Some of them have already had numerous failure experiences and want to prevent another one. They are so afraid of failing that they do not want to take the risk of trying.

Many adults assume that young people who are in trouble with the law or other authorities persist in using drugs simply because they are rebellious and defiant, which leads them to make poor choices. Although rebellion can be a factor, continued drug use usually is not simply an act of defiance, or a poor choice. There are other psychologically significant impediments to change, such as the ones listed above. If counselors were to insist upon immediate abstinence from youth in the earlier stages of change, their clients would likely drop out, lie, rebel, or fail. We must take this into account when setting expectations, defining progress and success, and thinking about accountability.

Even when defiance is part of the problem, it often represents a cover up for emotional distress, insecurity, and anxiety. Defiance may also be an aggressive response to a problematic relationship in the family, or with other adults. Demanding immediate abstinence could actually increase the level of defiance and an individual's determination to keep using drugs. It could aggravate relationship problems that gave birth to the rebellion in the first place. Because tightening the clamps works with so few individuals, and backfires with most, counselors must find additional, more productive ways, to confront defiant behavior.

Here's the dilemma:

If people in the earlier stages of change are admitted to programs demanding immediate abstinence, but then fail, they get another failure experience. We do not want that.

If they are admitted and allowed to keep using, they make a mockery of the admissions criteria. We do not want that either.

So, is it possible to screen out adolescents who are *not* ready, willing, and able to quit? Can we limit special concessions and special programs – such as drug courts, alternatives to incarceration, and alternatives to suspension from school — to young people who are advanced in the change process and really ready to quit? Is this a solution? Unfortunately it is not. First we do not have, and could not afford, all the necessary prison space to accommodate the rest of the population that is not ready, willing, and able to quit. Even if we could accommodate them, trying to predetermine which adolescents are ready to quit, and which are not, is a daunting diagnostic task – a slippery slope to climb. There is no before-the-fact assessment that can do this sort of screening. First, we have all the "fakers" who tell adults what they want to hear. Then, we have all the youth who may be frightened, shaken, and sincere when they say they intend to quit, but lack the staying power needed to sustain their determination. Then, we have all the young people who do not really understand what it takes to quit. They say they want to quit, but are unprepared when they face pressures and urges to use. Finally, we have young people who know what it takes to be successful, but severely overestimate their own ability to cope without drugs. In making initial assessments of youth, there is no reliable way to screen out those who are not ready, willing, and able to quit using drugs. Inevitably they will find their way into programs requiring abstinence.

What can we do about it? If young people are not fully prepared to make a sincere commitment to quit using drugs — and to succeed in their efforts – it makes little sense to get them to *say* they are going to quit. We need a different starting point. This, then, has implications for treatment providers, the criminal justice system, and other authorities who want to provide alternatives to incarceration or suspension from school.

TREATMENT

Young clients who are not ready, willing and able to quit may find themselves in situations (probation, drug courts, etc.) that require immediate abstinence. With these clients, the counselor role is not the same as that of law enforcement or corrections, or officials of the courts or the schools. Counselors do not mandate abstinence. They do *not* have the responsibility of trying to *make* someone quit using drugs. The counselor role is to help clients examine themselves and their situation, be aware of their alternatives, and make their own decisions. By staying out of the controlling role of trying to make their clients quit, counselors can identify themselves as allies, helping clients take charge of their own lives. In taking charge of their lives clients must consider the reality and contingencies of their situation, including the possible consequences for using drugs. They need someone who is truly their advocate; their ally in helping them think through their situation and in supporting them as they make their own decisions. So, counselors can serve as allies of clients who are being held accountable by courts, or schools, or juvenile corrections.

The mandate to be clean and sober is not really a pressing question for young people in residential treatment or juvenile correctional facilities. They do not need to make a decision to quit because they do not have the option of using. They are in a safe environment, with time to progress through The Seven Challenges in order to be ready to make their decisions to quit later, before they are discharged or released.

In contrast to residential settings, the "not using" issue is highly significant in outpatient treatment. One of the best strategies for counseling in situations that require abstinence is to validate the dilemma, as in:

> "This is really tough. You have a lot of pressure to quit using drugs. I'm not hearing that this is necessarily what you want to do, or something you feel ready to do. However, you're being watched and supervised and have all these pressures. Do you understand the consequences of drinking or using drugs? What do you think? What do you want to do about this? How do you want to handle the probation situation (school situation, court situation, etc.)?"

Some people who are not yet ready and prepared to make life changing decisions about the use of alcohol and other drugs of their own accord may recognize the need to strive for short term abstinence, for example, while on probation. If this possibility does not occur to them, counselors can point it out. It helps to make the distinction between "quitting" drug use on a long-term basis because it is a client's choice and "stopping" on a short-term basis, because it is a necessity to avoid the negative conse-quences for continued use.

Some youth will want to stop their drug use on a short-term basis. Counselors can help them grasp the realistic difficulty of this task. They can also try to inspire them to rise to the challenge – to use their will power, and test their self-control. Short-term stopping can be presented as an exercise in "sobriety sampling" – seeing what it is like to be straight and sober. The clients who choose to stop using drugs are given imme-diate help with "relapse prevention" skills. However, with The Seven Challenges Program, counselors would want to avoid the mistake of single-mindedly focusing on abstinence. It would be important to simultaneously start at the beginning, to lay a framework of understanding and skills that would support long-term success in life, and eventually more substantial decisions about drug use. We call this *working on two levels*: Clients go through The Seven Challenges from the beginning — laying a solid foundation for long-term success. At the same time, clients strive to be drug-free right away. This way, counselors accommodate clients who are required to demonstrate short-term abstinence and have chosen to comply with their mandate. For those clients who do not choose to comply with their mandate, counselors can help them anticipate and accept the consequences of continued drug use.

Thus, requiring abstinence can be helpful to three groups of youth: those who are ready to quit; those on the cusp of quitting; and those who are not ready and pre-pared, but recognize the necessity of abstinence and can give it their best shot, so to speak, on a short-term basis. This latter group is akin to children who engage in aggressive behavior toward other children, do not have a well developed sense of empathy, do not have a strong conscience, but can refrain from their aggressive behavior when they are threatened with restrictions and loss of privileges, or given external rewards, such as extra time on the computer, or a CD or DVD they want, or some other valued incentive. The motivation is entirely external, but could be strong enough to allow the child to gain some degree of self-control.

Working on two levels does spread the net just a little wider — to capture that subset of youth who are not ready to make substantial, significant changes in their lives, but at least want to give an all out effort to remain clean and sober on the short run. Realistically, however, many clients are not even ready for "working on two levels" when they first go for drug counseling. The best that could be expected from the rest of the clients – those who are incapable of working on two levels — would be *to make progress toward a decision to stop or quit.*

As stated earlier, clients who receive treatment in residential or correctional settings do not have to immediately decide to be clean and sober because they are not exposed to drugs, and do not have the option of using them. They have time to pre-pare for decisions about using drugs or not. In these settings, clients can usually progress through The Seven Challenges and be ready to make their decisions before they leave. But if they do have to leave before completing the program, these clients can also be presented with the option of working on two levels, and begin working in this manner before discharge. In correctional programs using The Seven Challenges, youth are routinely taught relapse prevention skills before they leave – so at least they are informed about it – regardless of the progress they have made in decision making about drugs.

THE COURTS, PROBATION, AND OTHER AUTHORITIES

Many judges and probation officers have been struggling with the complexity of the change process. They are tired of "false accountability" when youth say they will quit, but do not mean it. They have been thinking about progress and success in new ways, and about what standard to use in holding youth accountable. They are looking for effective programs and are often amenable to innovations.

The Seven Challenges approach works particularly well with youth who are under court supervision, or some sort of watchful eye. Young people know when someone in authority is watching them, and holding them accountable. Under these circumstances, skilled counselors can stick with their rightful role of helping young people evaluate their situation, which includes anticipating what negative consequences are likely to occur if they misbehave or use drugs, and how they will benefit from complying with the rules. Meanwhile the authorities create a system of contingencies that can tip the balance against harmful use of drugs. To be effective, individuals in positions of power (judges, probation officers, school authorities, etc.) have to know the youth with whom they work. Whenever possible, they demand abstinence of those who are capable of achieving it.

What about the youth who are not ready, willing, and able, and cannot "work on two levels?" The argument could be made that probation is a privilege (as is parole, or participation in drug court, or avoiding suspension in school). We could surely say to *all* youth: "You must stop – that's it. Deal with it. If you don't, the consequences will be (such and such). You must be abstinent. These are non-negotiable terms." The problem with this argument is that *by setting the bar at this high level, many youth will fail and be harmed by this experience.* Some may think they are willing to abstain (or fake it), but they are surely not prepared to succeed. Another problem is that there would not even nearly be enough beds in detention and correctional facilities to accommodate all the youth on probation who use drugs.

If authorities choose to cast a wider net to help more youth, including the large numbers who are in the earlier stages of change, then they must broaden their definition of progress and success. They cannot rely on a clean urine screen as the sole measure of success in overcoming drug abuse, and a dirty one as the only measure of failure. If authorities no longer employ a single measure for every youth — immediate success with immediate abstinence — then they need to rethink expectations and recalibrate measures of accountability.

RETHINKING EXPECTATIONS

What can be expected of youth in the earlier stages of change? Perhaps for them we can think in terms of "significant progress toward no drug use." Earlier in this publication we talked about redefining success in smaller increments in The Seven Challenges Program (pages 46-48). These same increments can be adapted to the purpose of measuring progress toward compliance with a legal requirement of abstinence.

Progress can be measured as youth move from the pre-contemplation stage, to contemplation, to preparation, and finally into action. It also can be measured as youth demonstrate effort and success in:

* working to establish an open and honest relationship with an adult who will assist them in counseling to become clean and sober (Challenge One);

* identifying what needs they have been trying to satisfy by using drugs, and, how they have used drugs to cope with life (Challenge Two);

* learning new skills to meet their needs such as problem solving skills, and certain coping skills (as taught throughout the Seven Challenges Program);

* showing increased understanding of harm and potential harm from their drug use (Challenges Three and Five);

* clarifying their values and setting goals for themselves (Challenges Five and Six);

* making sincere, informed, and internally motivated decisions to be clean and sober (Challenge Six);

* following through on their decisions to be clean and sober (Challenges Six and Seven).

Youth can also be recognized for their successful efforts as they complete the various journals in The Seven Challenges Program.

We want to hold individuals accountable to the highest standards they can attain: Either they need to be drug-free, or consistently demonstrate significant progress in that direction. This can be measured by some of the objectives mentioned above, and, for example by decreased numbers of positive drug screens. The criteria for progress and success will vary according to an individual's stages of change. Excessive tolerance would be a mistake. But unattainable goals are also damaging. In reality, many youth cannot attain immediate success with immediate abstinence.

PROBATION OFFICERS WEARING A SECOND HAT

Even with a rethinking of expectations and accountability, probation officers remain responsible for supervision of youth, which includes monitoring for compliance with laws and other conditions of probation. To maximize success with all youth, probation officers must recognize that youth pass through various stages of change on their road to recovery and to compliance with the conditions of probation. Probation officers can practice many of the counseling skills that help move youth through these stages of change, with of course certain modifications because of the supervision responsibilities. Knowing that their position of authority influences youth perceptions and responses to them, probation officers can nevertheless work to undo youth expectations about their role. Youth may see them as antagonists trying to "catch them" in violation of their probation. Probation officers can be clear that they do not wish to catch youth. Rather, they view their role as helping youth succeed in compliance. They want to be problem-solving partners in this endeavor. In that sense they wear a second hat, serving a counseling function. To the extent possible they will: work to create a climate in which youth can talk openly and honestly with them; really listen to youth to understand their point of view; help youth clarify the needs they have been satisfying or trying to satisfy with their drugs use; validate their reasons for drug use; help them identify the harm from their drug use; promote pro-social values; and teach life skills that can serve as an alternative to drug use. They will also help them identify future harm for their continued use of drugs, including possible consequences for violation of conditions of their probation. In other words, probation officers do not give up their supervisory role. Rather they increase their effectiveness by responding to the complexity of youth substance abuse and incorporating efforts to move youth through the stages of change. Youth effort and success in moving through the stages of change will surely have an influence on how probation officers respond to positive drug screens.

PROGRESS AND SETBACKS

Judges in drug courts have been among those who have led the way in recognizing the importance of identifying and reinforcing progress and success as a way of shaping positive behavior. They routinely reward successful behavior. They also respond appropriately to negative behavior. Probation officers are increasingly aware of the need to consider circumstances when responding appropriately to positive drug screens.

When behavior does not reach expected standards, judges and other authorities have many different ways they can respond. Alec Christoff, J.D., of the National Drug Court Institute,[27] suggests we think in terms of "responses" to substandard behavior, which is a neutral term, rather than the negative terms of consequences, sanctions, or punishment. Although some responses from people in positions of authority will be punitive in nature (such as jail time), not all of them are punitive. For example, responses to drug use might include assigning essays to be written, requiring more treatment, or assigning some sort of community service. We do not want young people to think of these activities as punishment. Rather, we want to build *good* feelings about expressing oneself in writing, getting counseling services, and making a contribution to one's community. It is not punishment to do more thinking about a problem, or to get additional professional help. It is something good! Similarly, community service should not be presented as punishment. Instead it should be presented as a way to repair harm and reconnect with one's community and sense of humanity.

With good supervision by the courts, failure to comply with court requirements should lead to a case sensitive *response*. The hammer is important. But the hammer must be appropriately gauged, fine-tuned, and calibrated. Honesty with a probation officer or the court can mitigate the response to a drug violation, as can demonstrated progress in moving through the stages of change in the direction of becoming drug free.

A SINGLE STANDARD WITH INDIVIDUALIZED RESPONSES

Some judges and other authorities may wish to give a single, clear message (for example: no drug use allowed) and feel compelled, for fairness sake, to set the same behavior standard for all youth (for example: abstinence). However, their responses to behavior that falls short of this standard (e.g., an incident of drug use) can take into consideration each person's different circumstance and stage of change. A judge might say: "You are all individuals. I will not respond in the same way to each of you. But it is my responsibility to make sure you are in compliance with the laws, including the drug laws." Judges can reward progress toward abstinence and still respond differently to positive drug screens, depending upon the circumstances. Youth who are not ready and prepared to succeed in being clean and sober are the ones who need the most help. An appropriate response for these individuals might be to increase the number of treatment sessions they will receive. Environmental considerations would also influence judicial responses. For example, youth from high-risk homes, with parents or other adults who abuse drugs, might be told to find a sponsor or a Big Brother or Big Sister, who could become a positive influence. Judges, probation officers and other authorities can also reinforce honesty by tempering their responses to young people who admit to drug use before they are detected by drug tests.

Ideally, when authorities supervise behavior, they establish their contingencies, and clearly explain and consistently enforce them in a case sensitive manner. A high standard is set both for the protection of society and for individual rehabilitation. The Seven Challenges counselor helps clients become aware of these contingencies, fully understand them, and ultimately make good choices.

DRAWING THE LINE

Working with youth in the earlier stages of change raises some important and frequently asked questions:

Is it enabling drug use if counselors have any degree of tolerance for the use of drugs while an individual is in treatment? The answer would be yes if they were allowing drug use by individuals who were ready and able to stop using. Tolerance, however, cannot be considered enabling when youth are in the earlier stages of change. Rather than enabling drug use, counselors are actually holding youth accountable to the highest attainable standard by insisting that they demonstrate progress along a continuum of change leading to the cessation of drug use.

Does this mean that youth who we know are using drugs may still remain in the community, for example under probation, and on parole? Does this mean that students who we know are using drugs might not be suspended from school while they are in treatment? Yes, it does mean that this can happen. This is nothing new, however, even in programs that insist upon immediate abstinence. In the current system, youth who are using drugs have no choice but to lie about it. They resist treatment and try to beat the system. In contrast, in The Seven Challenges Program these youth will get help in confronting their problem.

If some degree of drug use is tolerated as part of the change process with some individuals, or if court responses are not extreme in some cases when drugs are used, does this mean that the court has opened the gate to misconduct? Does this compromise public safety? Are there no limits? The answer is "no" to all these questions. There is no intended recommendation here that *all* youth should be offered alternatives to incarceration. Not all youth are good candidates for such programs. Some are not amenable to treatment. Some will keep using drugs at unacceptable levels, and pose a serious risk of harm to the community. They need to be incarcerated for public safety reasons and also to give them a clear message about compliance with laws. However, for the large remainder of youthful drug users, some degree of tolerance may be the only choice if they are to receive the help they need in treatment.

Counselors ask: What will the courts say if I do not demand immediate abstinence from my client? What will the P.O. say? What will my supervisor say? What will administrators in my agency say? In general, the fear about the responses of people on higher levels in a hierarchy of power, or of other authority figures, has been much greater than the reality of the response. Counselors have mostly received favorable responses when they have explained the stages of change and The Seven Challenges Program to supervisors, agency administration, probation officers, and the courts. Probation officers have had similar positive responses when they have explained the stages of change to judges. However, it is true that some individuals are locked into traditional practices that have not been shown to be effective. Nevertheless, counselors must strive for the integrity of their work if we are to advance the field.

"TRY TO MAKE ME QUIT" AND OTHER GAMES

"GO AHEAD, TRY TO MAKE ME QUIT"

When counselors engage in the mad rush for abstinence, adolescent clients often play the games of "Try to make me quit," "Try to prove that drugs are dangerous," "Try to prove that drugs have harmed me," "Try to prove that I've got a problem with drugs," and many variations of these basic games. They play these games to attain three different rewards:

- It is a way to get a lot of attention. The games can be played for long stretches of time.

- It gives them a sense of power. Adults are manipulated.

- It provides an outlet for anger and aggression. The games can frustrate and annoy adults.

Adult counselors are vulnerable to these games when they mistakenly believe, or act as if, their job is to convince young people that drugs are dangerous, and to make them quit. (They forget that the counselor's role is to help clients become aware of their options, to provide new options, and to help them make their own wise decisions.) When adults aggressively try to convince youth that (a) drugs are dangerous, and/or (b) that they (the adolescents) have been harmed by drugs, and/or that (c) they (the adolescents) need to quit using drugs, these adults give away their power. Adolescents identify adults with these misguided missions and can readily frustrate them by refusing to acknowledge drug dangers or harm, and by refusing to quit. When they refuse, adults lose the battle. It's quite simple: Adolescents have something the adults want (a decision to quit, or concession that they have been harmed). They can passively withhold it. Adolescents have found that they can cleverly engage adults in these games — involving prolonged discussions — because the adults are trying to reach their own goal of *making* youth decide to quit using drugs.

Adult moves in the game can be in the forms of lecture, argumentation, aggressive stances, or subtle attempts to outsmart the youth into their point of view. They may argue eloquently and/or vehemently about the dangers and harm from drugs, and the clients' need to quit. Often counselors tell clients that they are in denial. Clients are informed that they will not advance in the level system unless they "show progress." Counselors may take more aggressive positions, such as the threat, "You need to make progress in treatment or else.. ." The "or else" could be retention in treatment; or withholding or loss of privileges; or other consequences in the treatment setting. Quite often adults try to outsmart youth to prove their point. They think they will cleverly win the argument. However, there is always an answer. The dialogue evolves into the rebuttal cycle. (Examples: You play basketball, how well do you play now that you smoke marijuana? "Just as well and it's more fun"; What were your grades before – what are they now? "Now I can concentrate better and I can tolerate going to school"; What will happen when you are 18 and haven't finished high school? "I'll get a G.E.D."; It's bad for your lungs. "So is living in Phoenix, Houston and Los Angeles, but people do it"; How much did you use six months ago? How much is your current use compared to what it was six months ago? "I could quit whenever I want.")

Adolescents can initiate the game of "Try to make me quit" with moves such as these:

- "You keep telling me to quit. I could quit whenever I want to quit."

- "I know adults who do lots of drugs and they have jobs and they're doing fine."

- "My problem is no worse that the guy who drinks two beers at the end of the day."

- "I don't belong in this group. I only drink on weekends."

- "You haven't proved to me that marijuana is harmful. Actually it's harmless. It grows in the earth. It's natural."

- "I hear you say you have to drop all your old friends in order to be drug-free. Well, I'm going to quit and I'm going to keep my friends. I'm loyal to my friends. They've always been there for me. It's 'on me' to quit, not them."

- "I don't have a problem. I only use when I feel like it. At least it's not crack."

- "I just deal drugs. I don't use."

- "If I gave up drugs, I'd have to give up all the rituals that go with it – the fun of getting the drugs; hanging out; rolling joints, and all of that. That's asking too much."

Another variation of an opening move occurs when young clients say they have no drug problems, but then openly hint that they are going to pretend they have a problem and go through the motions of quitting, even though they will not really take it seriously. Clients try to draw counselors into the "convincing role" of proving that they really have a problem, need help, and need to follow their (the counselors') directions about quitting:

- "I only do ecstasy, a few joints, and pills. I don't drink and drive. It's not a problem. OK, just give me the book. Where's the book (*The Seven Challenges* reader)? Just give it to me and I'll do the work. (It's silly, but let's get it over with.)"

"TRY TO MAKE ME QUIT" IN GROUP SESSIONS

Young people can play "Try to make me quit" and its variants in one-to-one, family, or group sessions. It can be particularly rewarding in group settings because a lot of attention is given to the youth who play. Also, groups provide a showcase for youth who want to manipulate adults. Many drug-counseling group sessions have degenerated into one client after another playing these games with staff. The whole group time can be spent with counselors trying to convince first one youth, then another, and then the next that they have a drug problem, or need to quit. Youth just hold forth, saying, "You can't make me." Counselors who work in group settings must be especially alert to these games.

AN EXAMPLE OF TWO PLAYERS PLAYING "TRY TO MAKE ME QUIT"

The following is a dialogue between a client who is initiating a game of "Try to make me quit" and a counselor who is playing:

> Youth: I know adults who are older and have done drugs for years and they're fine. My drug of choice is acid. It's really not dangerous.

> You can get bad drugs on the street.

> Youth: Hasn't happened so far.

> We could show you O.D.'s at the hospital. People are killed. Some people are in nursing homes 24/7.

> Youth: I'm willing to run the risks.

> What do you like so much about acid?

> Youth: It's fun tripping. It's great at parties.

> Can't you have fun without it?

> Youth: Not this much fun!

> How many times have you used it?

> Youth: It's not like I count how many times. But I don't have a problem with it.

> Then, what got you here in treatment (or corrections)?

> Youth: Stealing cars.

> Were you tripping or high on some other drug?

> Youth: Yeah, but I would have done it anyway.

> Etc., etc.

HOW TO AVOID GAMES

The best prevention against playing these games with youth is:

1. Be clear about the counselor role. It is not to convince youth of anything or make them do anything.

2. Teach what it means to have 'working sessions' (pages 72-73).

3. Make sure that all sessions are working sessions. Calmly decline participation in these games, without rancor, as described below.

4. Redirect youth. Ask if he or she wants to "work on something" right now in this session.

When youth try to initiate a game of "Try to make me quit," counselors should respectfully decline to participate. This does not mean defiantly saying, "You're playing games. I won't participate." The art of the powerful reply is to address the issue briefly, and re-orient the individual to the purpose of the group.

For example: A young person says, "You haven't convinced me that marijuana is dangerous. It's a natural herb. It grows in the earth. It is completely harmless."

A model response to this youth would be the following:

> "Perhaps we have a misunderstanding here. You know, it's really not my job to convince you of anything. I'm not trying to convince you that marijuana is dangerous. I hope you understand this. However, I might add that I do disagree about it being harmless. I have seen many young people who have been hurt by smoking marijuana. Often they smoke so much that they are high all the time and don't learn how to deal with life. But as I said, I'm not here to try to convince you of anything. (Pause) If you want to look together at some of the marijuana literature about harm at some time, we can do that. But I have no intention of convincing you of anything. (Pause) Is there anything you would like to work on today in this session?
>
> "Well, I know lots of people who have never been hurt by marijuana."
>
> "As I said, I don't want to debate this. I'm not saying everyone is always harmed. But, I want to remind you that this is a working group. Do you want to work on something today? If not, let's move on so other group members have a chance to work."

In this exchange, the counselor briefly addressed the issues by (1) clarifying the counselor role (it is not to convince and control) and (2) giving an opinion on the particular issue (the danger of marijuana). Then the counselor reminded the youth that these are working sessions and offered the option of working on something in this session at that moment. The youth tried again to play the game, but the counselor held firm to the principle of doing work in a group session.

Counselors must remember the bigger picture. A mad rush for desired outcomes won't work. Often we have ample time to help a young person learn important lessons. We can plant seeds. We do not need young people to immediately provide their drug history, acknowledge harm, and say they will quit. We should not expect this. Clients are dragged to counseling sessions and often start with negative expectations about the process and negative attitudes toward counselors. We need to back off, take a deep breath, build trust, and work on relationship issues first. But if counselors are rushed and vested in convincing youth about harm, danger, and the need for immediate abstinence — on their own timing — they will lose the power struggle. When young people are playing games such as "Try to make me quit," we can never convince them of anything. They want us to try because they know they can frustrate us. We need to step back and stay focused on what is supposed to happen in groups. Young people are supposed to work on themselves and their issues. If youth are being defensive about some aspect of harm, danger, or abstinence, counselors can remember the particular issue for future reference and address it later, in a constructive, non-game context.

WHEN GROUP MEMBERS CHALLENGE OTHER GROUP MEMBERS WHO ARE PLAYING "TRY TO MAKE ME QUIT"

In working groups, some group members may be angered by peers who try to play the game of "Try to make me quit," or one of its variations.

For example, one group member may be initiating the game by saying, "I don't have a drug problem. I only use drugs to have fun with my friends. I only do drugs when I'm partying...and I don't get in trouble."

Peers may start confronting this youth; pointing out ways that the person has been harmed, or contradicting assertions about only minimal drug use. Sometimes peers have witnessed drug use that the person is now denying, or heard that individual boast about greater drug use. Some of this information may be quite revealing. In general, it is good when peers point out harm, so that adults do not have to do it. However, counselors still want to avoid creating a climate of pressure and harsh confrontation. It may make sense to let a little feedback slip by. But soon the counselor should be clear to group members: None of us should try to convince others of their problems. We can share our opinions and give our feedback. But it is not our responsibility to tell people they have problems or to fix them. We are not here to convince anybody of anything. We want to create a climate in which people look at their own lives.

SELF-DISCLOSURE

Another game that youth like to play with counselors is called, "You can't help me." In some respects this game is quite similar to "try to make me quit" because counselors are challenged to prove their worth. Clients initiate this game with statements such as the ones below, expressed not as curiosity about the counselor, but challenges to their credentials:

"How can you help me? You've never gotten high."

Or, the opposite:

"How can you help me? I know what you do on Saturday night. You're out getting loaded or getting high."

Counselors who do not recognize these power plays may play along by defending themselves. They may give answers such as the following, some of which may be accurate and some fictionalized:

- I used when I was younger. I had problems and solved them. I know a thing or two.

- I used, but never abused drugs. I know about drugs.

- I have friends who did drugs, so I know.

- I have a problem with weight, so I understand these types of problems.

- Even though it's true I never used, I still can help you.

Or, counselors may try to throw it right back at youth with a harsh tone:

- It's not about me; it's about you.

- It's none of your business what I do on Saturday night.

- You have no idea what I do on Saturday night.

- You don't know what I have or have not done. We're here to work on you, so stop this nonsense.

Either way – from a defensive position or an aggressive one — these responses are playing the game. The point is that youth have challenged the counselors — challenged their competency — and the counselors feel a need to either defend themselves or strike back. Under these circumstances, self-disclosure is futile. Consider these examples:

Youth: How can you help me? You've never gotten high. You don't know what it's like.

Counselor: I have used drugs. I know what it's like. I can help you.

Youth: Well then, you used drugs and now you're fine. I'm using them now...and I'll be fine, too. So this is ridiculous.

Youth: How can you help me? You get high, too. You're not fooling me.

Counselor: I have never used drugs in my life.

Youth: Well then, you have no idea what it's like. You definitely can't help me.

Rather than self-disclosing in response to a power play, it is more appropriate to expose the game and refuse to play. For example:

"Look, it sounds as though you are doubting my ability to help you. I can assure you that I am good at what I do, that is, drug counseling, regardless of what I may or may not have ever done with drugs. I'm a good listener. (If it's true, you can add: I have helped many young people with drug problems.) If you want to doubt me, it's your prerogative. Nothing I can do about it. But if you give it a chance, I think you will see that I can be very helpful to you. That's up to you. I would like to help you. I hope you choose to accept my help."

Youth: "Well, do you use drugs?"

"As I said, the issue you seem to be raising is whether I can help you. I believe I can. That's up for you to decide whether you want to give it a try. I believe I can be helpful. However, I do not choose to talk with you about whether I have or have not used drugs."

Challenging statements such as the "You can't help me...." type should be differentiated from sincere, and understandable client interest and curiosity in knowing about their counselors. Sometimes clients are just curious about counselors and want to know them better. So, they ask personal questions, including about counselor drug use. This raises the issue of self-disclosure: To what extent should counselors working with youth talk about their personal life, in this case, with regard to their own alcohol and other drug use? The field is divided on this matter.

Strong arguments can be made about the benefits of "telling your story" i.e., sharing one's own personal experiences. It could solidify a relationship, provide inspiration, or enhance credibility of certain recommendations (because "I've lived it myself.") On the other hand, establishing boundaries keeps the focus on youth and not the counselor. Whether counselors have used or not is really not the big issue. When people put themselves forward as role models, they can undermine relationships and lose credibility ("Well, you used when you were young and you're fine now; I'll be fine, too"). Also counselors may wish to maintain their legitimate privacy.

Some agencies have policies about boundaries and self-disclosure. If an agency does not have policy, individuals and co-workers should think ahead and anticipate how they will choose to respond to inevitable questions of this sort.

The Seven Challenges Program does not take a position on self-disclosure. However, those who self disclose should be certain that they are considering first the needs of their own clients (not their own recovery, or ego). They should be focused on helping youth, not on simply "being liked." They should be aware that telling one youth is the same as telling all of them in a program because word will spread. They should consider the impact of their self-disclosure on other practitioners who may not wish to disclose.

Counselors who choose not to self disclose should do so courteously and politely, without making harsh rejecting statements in harsh tones that hurt clients ("We're here to work on YOU. My life is not your concern.") They do not have to justify the decision not to self disclose, other than saying that it is their choice. For example: "I have chosen not to discuss my personal issues in my work. I realize that might disappoint you because you want to know more about me. That is my choice. I am confident, however, that I can help you."

Clients might respond: "Well, you're asking me to talk about my life." If so, counselors can politely remind clients that this is precisely the purpose of these sessions, which is to help clients look at their lives and discuss it with their counselor.

The Seven Challenges Manual   ©2004 Robert Schwebel, Ph.D.

SEVEN CHALLENGES GENDER ISSUES

GENDER RESPONSIVE CONSIDERATIONS

The Seven Challenges Program was developed from experiences working with both boys and girls. As such, it could be considered gender neutral. However, there are special gender responsive considerations when using this program with either sex. Some of these considerations are discussed below.

SEVEN CHALLENGES FOR GIRLS

With girls, special considerations include the following:

Female socialization is to value relationships. Girls want to relate; they want to feel needed and connected.

The traditional female sex role is to focus on others; to nurture; to give.

Little girls are socialized to be "nice" – sweet, cute and polite.

When angry, girls may be labeled as a "bitch," or put down in other ways. Self-assertion is categorized as selfishness.

Aggression is often channeled inwardly; sometimes involving self-harm and self-mutilation.

Aggression is also expressed by harming relationships.

Bullying is less physically aggressive with girls than boys, but still prevalent, often taking the form of exclusion ("don't want you in my group" or "you can't come to my party"), gossiping, talking behind someone's back, ridicule, and rejection. Girls are more prone than boys to roll their eyes as a put down.[28]

Many girls are victims of sexual abuse and other trauma: Current estimates are that 70-90% of girls in the juvenile justice system have been abused.[29] Girls who are sexually abused are three times more likely to abuse drugs.

When behavior does become aggressive, it is often motivated by prior victimization.

In our culture, an inordinate amount of status is based on the bodies and physical appearances of females. Yet the culture only allows for a very narrow range of what is defined as attractive or beautiful. This problem is reinforced by media images and the idea of the perfect Barbie doll.

Sexism strikes hard against self-esteem and a sense of personal power. Girls need an opportunity to develop a voice.

IMPLICATIONS FOR GIRLS WITH REGARD TO THE SEVEN CHALLENGES

The Seven Challenges is a relationship-based program in which counselors are trained to avoid contentious arguments with young clients. Counselors align themselves with youth as problem-solving partners: helping them examine their own lives and make their own decisions, and empowering them by giving more options. As such, The Seven Challenges Program leads to caring, connected relationships. This is especially important to girls who have been socialized to value relationships. It is also an empowerment model, something that is important to any group that has suffered from unfair power imbalances. It gives girls a voice, which is something they need. Girls build self-esteem as they learn to make their own, independent, wise choices.

Carol Gilligan[30] has pointed out that the classic psychological models of development, such as Erikson's view of identity formation, were based largely on studies of boys. Gilligan stresses the importance of relationships in girls' lives. The formation of a girl's mature identity cannot be based solely on separation from parents, but must also include an enduring relationship with adults who are committed and care about her.

There are some special issues to consider with each challenge when working with girls.

CHALLENGE ONE AND GIRLS

Challenge One is very much the relationship-based challenge.

Girls have been taught to value relationships and should be responsive to this. They will benefit from work about safety and establishing trust in relationships — and opening up and supporting one another. Also, girls may respond more positively to the program and to journaling than boys because they tend to be more introspective about experiences and their personal lives.

Girls bullying behavior often takes the form of gossip, ridicule, and rejection. This means that special care is required to make groups safe, and to protect group members from this behavior. In Challenge One, youth will learn about program rules that protect confidences and forbid verbal aggression. Counselors should be clear about the rules that protect program participants. One important rule concerns confidentiality: "What's said in group, stays in group." This means no gossiping or discussion of group issues outside of the sessions. An extension of that rule is: *"No verbal bullying allowed."* No one is allowed to use personal information as a put-down, as gossip, or as a weapon against other program members when they are hurt or angry, or under any circumstance *during a group session, or outside of group. Program participants cannot ever use information as aggression against someone when they are angry, or want to hurt them, or under any circumstances.* Counselors should stress that these group rules are strictly enforced, and be clear about the serious consequences that will be imposed for violations. Violations of these rules against emotional bullying are among the most serious, on a par with violations of rules against physical bullying. Groups must be safe: Program participants must feel free to open up and talk honestly about themselves.

Throughout the program young people will have opportunities to learn cooperative communication, including positive ways to express anger or other emotions, without causing harm to others. This is a positive alternative to the abuse of information as aggression. Another positive alternative is the concept of sisterhood and mutual support. More and more females are finding ways to unite and support one another.

CHALLENGE TWO AND GIRLS

Challenge Two is about the benefits of drug use. Girls often use drugs for reasons that differ from those that motivate boys. When the sexes are compared, teenage girls more often use drugs to relieve stress or alleviate depression, whereas boys are more likely to do it for thrills or heightened social status. Also, as girls go through puberty, they are likely to compare themselves physically and academically to their peers, increasing the doubts they feel about themselves. Girls more often than boys have dissatisfaction with their body images. One girl said, "This face (her own) won't win any beauty contests. I use drugs to feel pretty." Drug use by girls may be connected to problems of low self-esteem.

It has also been found that many girls first use drugs with boyfriends. So girls will need help sorting out their own feelings about drugs from their desires to please partners, or join in with drug using friends. Real or perceived pressure from boyfriends may be a significant factor in the use of drugs by girls.

CHALLENGE THREE AND GIRLS

Challenge Three is about harm from drugs. Girls and young women get hooked on alcohol and other drugs more quickly than boys, and they get hooked using lesser amounts. They also suffer the consequences faster and more severely.[31] Also, girls are more likely to prostitute themselves, trading sex for drugs.

CHALLENGE FOUR AND GIRLS

Challenge Four has special relevance for girls because this is the challenge that considers the social context of drug use – including the oppressive factors or disadvantages, and limitations or lack of opportunities that contribute to the development of serious problems in life. The influence of sexism causes girls to be raised with doubts about worth and value as a female; with a preoccupation about physical appearance and body image; with messages not to be smarter than boys, and not to be assertive. In relationships girls are taught to be polite, please others, put others first, and be selfless. When they are strong they are seen as bitches. When they stick up for themselves, they are seen as selfish. All of these factors hurt girls, and can explain why they may turn to drugs.

Challenge One emphasized creating safe, caring relationships. In Challenge One, and again in Challenge Four, young clients may be asked to consider when in their lives trust was broken; how they felt; and how they responded.

CHALLENGE FIVE AND GIRLS

Challenge Five is about the future. The traditional female sex role has largely been defined in terms of relationships to males. Girls have not been given as many career options and opportunities as boys, nor given encouragement to think about career achievement. In fact, girls sometimes fear that by outperforming boys they would compromise their attractiveness to the opposite sex. It is important that girls see broader horizons and more opportunities. This challenge supports them in that. Also, girls who are involved in traditional relationships dominated by males may find it harder to know their own values. Values clarification is part of Challenge Five.

CHALLENGE SIX AND GIRLS

Challenge Six is especially important to girls who need a voice. This is their opportunity to define themselves and make their own choices.

CHALLENGE SEVEN AND GIRLS

Challenge Seven is about making successful changes. In avoiding drug relapse, girls may need extra help in learning to resist males who are using drugs and perhaps pushing them toward use. People need support in making significant changes in their lives. This challenge is an opportunity for girls to develop a sense of sisterhood, through mutually supportive relationships with one another.

SKILL BUILDING FOR GIRLS

Skill building is an important part of The Seven Challenges Program. Certain skills, discussed below, may be especially important for girls. These considerations could be addressed either in girls-only, or co-ed groups.

Girls are socialized to please and demur to males and to view self-assertion as selfishness. They need special help with assertiveness skills, including support in identifying their needs and making them known; and support in developing their own female voice. Girls may show their resentment through plotting, grudges, and subtle social exclusion. They need help with communication skills, especially for expressing hurt and angry feelings in direct and assertive ways. Girls may let interpersonal problems seethe beneath the surface, sometimes plotting revenge but doing little to confront the problem. They need special help with conflict resolution.

Because physical appearance may be the focus of self-image issues, and because girls get less encouragement to consider a wide variety of careers, values clarification and help with self-esteem issues are important services for girls.

Because of the high rate of victimization, girls have special needs for trauma recovery services.

SEVEN CHALLENGES FOR BOYS

With boys, special considerations include the following:

> More often than girls, boys use drugs to prove themselves, for thrill seeking, and to attain social status with peers. They want to appear macho. This can lead to bingeing behavior.

> Boys place a high value on appearing tough and avoiding appearances of vulnerability.

Boys often think of power in limited terms, with an emphasis on aggressive behavior.

Boys often cover up emotions, especially ones they consider "soft" or vulnerable such as pain, sadness, or hurt. They may not be aware of what they feel, and then use drugs to cope with emotions about which they have little or no awareness.

Because boys cover up emotions, there is a great deal of hidden depression in boys.

Boys are concerned about appearing weak. Hurt boys say, "So what?" They want to appear tough, and fear being seen as "soft." Boys sometimes hide pain by committing crimes and doing drugs. These activities may be pathways to violence.

Boys may see it as weakness to want help, or accept it.

Boys tend to have open power struggles in a group setting.

Boys are often taught a type of super-individualism. They may consider it a sign of weakness to open up in counseling.

Many boys feel very alone, and may secretly desire to open up and connect with others.

IMPLICATIONS FOR BOYS WITH REGARD TO THE SEVEN CHALLENGES

In The Seven Challenges Program, young people make their own decisions. This framework should be emphasized because it is important to boys who may be especially resistant to requesting or accepting help from others. They want to be in charge, and in fact, should take increasing control over their own decision making process as they move through adolescence.

The *holistic* approach of The Seven Challenges is especially beneficial to boys because it provides opportunities for them to build emotional literacy and learn important relationship skills. The program requires a great deal of introspection, which helps with emotional literacy.

The Seven Challenges Counseling Approaches serve as a model of cooperative relationships and demonstrates a different type of power from the type of power many youth – especially boys — are accustomed to experiencing – i.e., it demonstrates ways of being powerful without using aggressive and harsh confrontational tactics.

There are some special issues to consider with each challenge when working with boys.

CHALLENGE ONE AND BOYS

There are special obstacles for engaging boys in Challenge One. Boys tend to be less introspective than girls. They may believe that accepting professional help is a sign of weakness. They may be worried about status and image, and see it as "soft" to identify feelings. They are reluctant to admit vulnerability. Although they are prone to posture "tough," many boys are privately worried about their direction in life and sense of aloneness. Many feel very isolated and frightened, and secretly want to open up and connect with others. Challenge One is an opportunity to develop a safe and supportive atmosphere to engage and induce boys into the change process. Guest Status (see page 81) works particularly well with defiant, oppositional boys because it is a way they can back off and save face in a group session, without getting hooked in an escalating power struggle when they first start in the program. Boys need counselors to back off and move slowly so that they can gradually relax and feel safe in a treatment setting.

CHALLENGE TWO AND BOYS

There is a good deal of hidden depression in boys. They may be unaware of mood problems, yet be self-medicating without conscious awareness. Challenge Two is an opportunity for boys to gain emotional literacy, especially about their own feelings. Also boys often use drugs to prove themselves, impress others, and gain social status with peers. More often than girls, they are thrill seekers. Boys will identify these needs when working on this challenge. Boys also may recognize that their drug use is associated with other behaviors that are oppositional and defiant. This opens the door to learn new and more positive ways of being strong and independent.

CHALLENGE THREE AND BOYS

In posturing tough and showing off, boys are more likely to openly resist or oppose treatment, especially when counselors talk about the harm from drugs, or the need to quit. Boys are more prone than girls to play games such as: "Try to make me quit"; or "Try to prove that drugs have harmed me." These games give them attention and the sense of power they may crave so very much. Counselors trained in the Seven Challenges Counseling Approaches will not engage in these games. Instead, they will help boys reduce their defensiveness as they consider the harm from drugs.

Because boys show-off and try to gain status with their drug use, they may drink large amounts of alcohol or use large amounts of drugs. More than girls, they represent a special risk for potential harm from bingeing and excesses. Under these circumstances, they are at higher risk for drinking and driving, and for engaging in sexually risky behavior. This potential for harm will become clear during work on this challenge.

CHALLENGE FOUR AND BOYS

Boys may be driven to use drugs in response to social pressures to perform, to prove themselves, or to be tough. They may be frustrated in school achievement, which is supposed to lead them to success in the role of "male as provider." Too often parents, and other adults, have high demands and expectations, but provide insufficient support. Boys also may be criticized for asking for help, or perceived as weak for expressing feelings and showing emotional sensitivity. This sort of sex role scripting leaves them vulnerable to using drugs for any number of reasons; such as to numb themselves, to forget about pressures to perform, to fend off negative self-talk; to get out feelings they may repress, or to show off.

CHALLENGE FIVE AND BOYS

Challenge Five is about the future. Frustrations in achievement may contribute to drug problems. By the same token, the desire to achieve can be marshaled as a force to help boys think about future career and education.

CHALLENGE SIX AND BOYS

Challenge Six is the decision making challenge. Many boys are struggling for a sense of power. This program speaks to their urge for independence and empowers them to make their own choices. Boys also learn the importance of getting help and support, and overcoming tendencies to try to "be tough" and do it all alone.

CHALLENGE SEVEN AND BOYS

The reasons for drug use identified in Challenge Two are also the risk factors for drug use in Challenge Seven. Boys have sometimes built their reputation on their ability to consume large amounts of alcohol or other drugs. To avoid relapse, they will have to find new ways to feel good about themselves and proud in front of their peers. This challenge is an opportunity to use their own strong willpower, and to combine it with support from people who care about them. Boys can learn to look to others for support and overcome tendencies toward super-individualism. Many boys drink to calm social anxiety or self medicate against depression. They will need to problem solve to reduce social anxiety and other negative emotions. They will also need to implement new coping skills.

SKILL BUILDING FOR BOYS

Boys are trained to "be tough" which often includes the idea of cutting off emotions. Boys need help in emotional literacy: learning to identify, value, label and express their own feelings. They also need help in listening and recognizing the feelings of others, and increasing sensitivity to the feelings of others. The one feeling males are often free to express is anger and resentment, though too often this takes excessively aggressive and undisciplined forms. Boys need help in anger management: learning to control aggressive impulses, and to communicate anger and resentment in disciplined and respectful ways. Because of reinforcement of dominant and aggressive behavior, boys need help in learning about loving, respectful, and cooperative relationships, and in conflict management. Boys need to develop their caring and nurturing skills. This includes increasing their awareness, sensitivity and respect to the thoughts and feelings of others. It means learning to share and cooperate in relationships, rather than seeking to win and gain control. Boys need to understand, too, that they can be powerful, without relying always on physical force or "in-the-face" types of power. Finally, boys often have issues related to self-esteem – trying to impress others, or feeling shame about hidden depression, or problems related to achievement. They need help with self-esteem issues.

SUPERVISION

ISSUES

FIDELITY OF IMPLEMENTATION AND TREATMENT

To insure fidelity of implementation of The Seven Challenges Program there are a number of critical issues to consider. Some of the program implementation and clinical supervision issues are outlined below. They are organized in different categories, although you will notice a great deal of overlap.

PROGRAM IMPLEMENTATION

AGENCY ISSUES

Goals: Agency personnel fully understand what it entails to do The Seven Challenges Program. They provide initial and follow-up training for all counselors and line staff. Counselors and staff understand, embrace, and communicate the spirit of the program. The agency provides adequate services and appropriate structure. They provide adequate safeguards of private and confidential information.

Potential Problems:

- Some agencies think that implementing the Seven Challenges Program simply means having youth read the books and use the journals. They think that counseling sessions will consist of reading and perhaps talking about the reading, and writing. They do not understand that these materials are tools, and only one aspect of a comprehensive program.

- Clinical staff may not be adequately trained – lacking initial and adequate follow up training and supervision. This can be due to staff turnover or inadequate funding for necessary training.

- Line staff may not be adequately oriented to the program and trained. They don't know the goals, philosophy and strategy of the program. They may be unclear on their own role. Line staff acceptance and enthusiasm are important. Without proper orientation and training, they will probably work at cross-purposes with the clinical staff (For example, arguing with youth and trying to convince them they have problems). Also, youth ask for feedback from adults on various issues in their journals. Staff must understand the program.

- Boundary deficiency: Inadequate separation or distinction between behavior management, which may be highly controlled, and counseling which requires a climate of free thinking without excessive fear of consequences for thoughts, feelings, and disclosures.

- Line staff may especially be confused about the "two hats they wear" because they are responsible for behavioral management much of the time, but also participate in counseling sessions at other times.

- Expectations may be set too high for the length of stay of youth: Services are programmed to move too fast because of the short length of stay of clients. This occurs most often when the funding and program structure determine the pace, rather than clinical judgment.

- The spirit of the program is absent: tone of the interactions with youth is too confrontational; too much emphasis on convincing youth about drug dangers and rushing them to quit; not enough validation of youth experiences; too much emphasis on striving for adult goals rather than on helping young people make their own decisions and finding self-motivation to change; overemphasis on drugs, with not enough emphasis on co-occurring issues, lifestyle issues, problem-solving, and empowering by teaching life skills; youth see counselors more as adversaries than allies. This problem is either a function of inadequate training and supervision or lack of acceptance of the model.

- Lack of safeguards of information that youth self disclose. Young people get in trouble because of what they say in sessions.

- Services are too regimented, and not responsive to youth interests and emerging needs.

- Atmosphere is too permissive: Because immediate abstinence is not required, counselors sometimes do not set a high enough standard in terms of work in sessions and the need for other behavioral changes, short of abstinence.

- Full spectrum of services not provided: Seven Challenges Discovery Groups; Seven Challenges Lifestyle Action Groups; Journaling Time; trauma recovery services; family services; life skills training.

- Not enough intensity of services for youth who need more help.

- Not enough individualized attention to match the needs of all youth.

- No one made responsible to ensure the fidelity of implementation of program components and counseling strategies.

- Not enough continuing training and supervision. Initial enthusiasm about the program is not supported by ongoing supervision and training.

- Deficiency in clinical skills.

COUNSELOR ISSUES

Goals: Counselors are aware of their own perspective on drugs and have openness to really listening to their clients' point of view. They maintain calm objectivity about drug benefits and harm. Counselors will need courage to go against political, parental, and social pressure to promise to deliver drug-free youth overnight. They must be patient and help young people: identify the needs they satisfy, or attempt to satisfy, by using drugs; learn life skills; identify harm from drugs, without engaging in power struggles; see options; make decisions; and successfully follow through.

Potential Problems:

- Lack of awareness of personal lens through which drug use is evaluated. Many counselors have an unconscious tendency to impose their own values on youth. Some counselors may be rigid or panicky about drug use. This reaction could be due to their own past problems with drugs, or the problems of other important people in their lives, or even to their own fears about drugs. Other counselors may under-react and underestimate the potential harm from drugs, perhaps due to their own experiences of using in moderation, or because they have seen many people use drugs in moderation without harm. These predilections make it hard for them to calmly listen and respond appropriately to youth.

• Many, if not most, counselors will say that they are not trying to convince clients to quit using and that they are willing to calmly listen to what youth like about drugs. But when they actually sit with clients, their behavior does not match their claims. They cannot tolerate clients talking freely about the benefits of drugs without getting uncomfortable, interrupting, or arguing. They still end up trying to persuade young people to quit, or even arguing with them. They play the games of "Try to convince me" or "Try to make me quit." They get caught in the rebuttal cycle. Without conscious awareness of what they are doing, they engage in a mad rush for abstinence, putting pressure on youth to quit immediately.

• Counselor fears: Fearfulness about embracing this program because it does not require immediate abstinence of all youth, as reflected in comments made by counselors such as these: "This makes sense, but... What will the judge say? What will the probation officer say? What will my supervisor say?" This can reflect emotional difficulty in moving to this innovative program; lack of acceptance of the model; personal problems with authority figures; and with some counselors, a frightened reaction to a real and difficult situation.

• Counselors not doing the required work. Many counselors in the field of substance abuse treatment feel that they are overworked. For this, or other reasons, counselors sometimes do not invest the effort that is required to succeed in a program of this nature. For example:

It is important to prepare for Seven Challenges Groups, so that discussions and activities are relevant to youth – their current issues and the bigger picture of what needs to be done at a particular moment.

It is important that counselors invest the energy required to respond extensively to journal writing. If counselors are brief or cursory in their journal responses, youth will view the work as trivial (counselors aren't much interested), and as another hoop through which they are required to jump. Journal work will be trivialized and the whole program discounted by youth.

It is important that counselors study and really know *The Seven Challenges* book, so they can draw upon it when it is relevant.

• Counselors not knowledgeable enough about co-occurring problems.

• Counselors not knowledgeable enough about drug issues.

CLINICAL ISSUES SPECIFIC TO THE SEVEN CHALLENGES COUNSELING APPROACH

ORIENTING YOUTH TO THE PROGRAM AND CONTINUALLY INTEGRATING THE CLIENTS' WORK WITH THE SEVEN CHALLENGES PROCESS

Goals: Counselors help young people understand The Seven Challenges process, embrace it in their efforts at making good decisions, and see how it has bearing on the all the work that they are doing during the counseling process.

Potential Problems:

- Counselors may not sufficiently promote and excite youth about the program and/or materials. This may reflect their own lack of enthusiasm (which would need to be addressed) or their style of presentation (which needs to be developed).

- Ineffective or inadequate initial orientation of youth to the program and to the Seven Challenges themselves. This could be an agency oversight, or an error made by a counselor who fails to provide the overview.

- Not sufficiently teaching the process, or reinforcing the process, or reminding youth of the process to keep it "out there" in their minds as they work on various issues

- The work in each and every counseling session is not being related to The Seven Challenges' process.

- Posters are not hanging in rooms where sessions are held, or not being used as a reference point during sessions.

CONFUSION ABOUT COUNSELOR ROLE

Goal: Counselors undo negative expectations about their role. (They are seen as trying to control youth and make them quit.) They establish themselves as a problem-solving partner.

Potential Problems:

- Not proactively undoing youth expectation that the counselor's job is to make them quit using drugs.

- Too often counselors themselves feel very strongly that their job is to get youth to quit using drugs. Young clients see them as taking something away – not giving them more skills and options.

- Counselors not introducing and presenting themselves as problem-solving partners.

- Correct introduction of the counselor role, but counselor not sticking to the role — getting hooked into the mad rush for abstinence and playing games such as "Try to make me quit."

RELATIONSHIP SKILLS

Goals: Counselors establish warm, empathic relationships, with good listening that inspires young people to feel safe and talk openly. They respond to power plays in powerful ways without getting in power struggles. They challenge and inspire youth to think clearly and take charge of their lives.

Potential Problems:

Too hard with youth

- Locking horns and getting into power struggles with youth about behavior or topics discussed in group.

- Not enough empathy and connectedness with youth.

- Conscious or unconscious tendency to be impatient and argumentative; trying to convince, persuade, and cajole youth to change their behavior.

- Hooked into playing games such as: "Try to convince me that I've been harmed by drugs"; "Try to make me quit."

- Not good at drawing youth out and listening.

- Do not inspire youth or give them hope about change.

Too soft with youth.

- Too permissive. Not enough expectation of positive behavior in group.

- Counselors sometimes do not see the need for behavior change during the counseling process. Because this program defers decisions about drugs, counselors may think that all changes can be deferred. This can lead to excessive contemplation and not enough action.

- Expectations of behavioral change are set too low – not enough learning new skills; not enough problem-solving.

- Not fully using the leverage from the relationship for caring confrontation.

TOO FOCUSED ON DRUG USE

Goals: Counselors address the issue of drug abuse and dependence, but within the broad context of an individual's life, experiences, and environment.

Potential Problems:

- Sometimes counselors put too much focus on drug use – and not enough focus on (a) building the counseling relationship and (b) other aspects of a person's life. They do not pay enough attention to non-drug problems and to teaching basic life skills. They find it hard to focus on other issues, besides drugs. The Seven Challenges addresses the drug issue, but never narrowly, out of context of the lives of young people.

- Not thinking holistically (Related to previous item): Not enough focus on anger management, stress management, assertiveness training, relaxation training, impulse
control, and other life skills.

- Clients not getting sufficient help with co-occurring problems.

DISCUSSION OF DRUG BENEFITS

Goal: Counselors allow youth to freely talk about drug benefits.

Potential Problems:

- Counselors are uncomfortable allowing discussion of the benefits of drugs. They cut it off prematurely, or find themselves arguing about the negatives, or trying to entice young people to focus on the negatives. They cannot allow a free flowing discussion of positives.

- Counselors may confuse both 'thinking about' and 'reminiscing over' past pleasures in front of a group with 'telling war stories' or 'euphoric recall.' These activities should be differentiated. Identifying drug benefits, including from the pleasure of drugs, is part of the work. Bragging, boasting, comparing, exaggerating, glamorizing, or telling war stories are all something different.

- Counselor difficulty in accepting and validating why people use drugs – helping them make sense of their own motivation.

- Counselor difficulty in accepting that some young people use drugs simply for pleasure – perhaps not to cover up problems, etc., or due to peer pressure or anxiety or depression.

ABOUT THE HARM FROM DRUGS

Goal: Counselors bring up the discussion of harm from drug use and let clients become aware of the harm, without locking horns, getting argumentative, increasing the defensiveness of clients, and engaging in power struggles.

Potential Problems:

- Lack of finesse in bringing up harm.

- Counselors exaggerating dangers.

- Trying to convince youth of dangers – either pounding away, or trying to cleverly outsmart them into thinking that drugs are dangerous, and that clients need to quit using.

- Don't provide space for youth to come up with own recognition of harm.

- Too much pressure: Cannot probe and back-off. Instead: Probe and then more and more and more pressure.

- Don't back off when appropriate; piling on arguments against drugs, which increases client resistance.

- Drug education is narrowly focused on harm from each drug, which increases client resistance.

- Confused about chemical dependency; label drug abuse as addiction or dependence.

APPLYING PRESSURE TO QUIT

Goal: Counselors establish the laid back position of helping young people make their own decisions.

Potential Problems:

- Impatience and pressure for the decision to quit.

- Counselors insist upon abstinence – not establishing smaller increments of success. This may be evident in the selection of treatment goals and in client/counselor interaction.

- Trying to convince young people to quit.

- Playing the authority role rather than the counseling role.

- Lack of time perspective: Seems to be going for the "one session fix;" can't back off when appropriate and slow the rush.

- Trying to "outtalk" clients, win with words, so to speak.

VALIDATION AND COMPASSION

Goal: Counselors help young people put their own experiences in context; to see ways in which they have been harmed or deprived of opportunities; also, to empower people to take responsibility for their own share of a problem, and to do something about it. Balancing a critical look at the environmental situation of individuals with their own self-criticism.

Potential Problems:

Counselors may be overly critical of youth; too blaming

- A tendency to over-label, either with a psychiatric label or with other labels, such as "druggie," "addict," or "troublemaker."

- Excessively attributing all misbehavior to weak will, or weak character, or moral failing.

- Overly inclined to define problems in terms of "criminal thinking."

- Blame oriented; sees the problems as all within the individual.

- Not seeing social and situational causes of problems.

- Not looking for validation and providing validation for youth for their behavior.

- Confuses validation with justification, causing counselors to have difficulty accepting youth behavior and validating it.

Counselors may make too many excuses; setting the bar too low

- Blaming the world for everything and not helping young people take responsibility for their own share of a problem.

- Making too many excuses: Not expecting youth to take responsibility for their behavior and its effects on themselves and others.

- Too "all-accepting;" not teaching responsibility and accountability.

- Allowing justification for misbehavior.

- Buys into "poor me" and "everyone is mistreating me" type of victim role, as differentiated from *real* abuse and victimization.

- Not enough constructive criticism, not enough challenging of clients.

DECISION-MAKING

Goal: Counselors help youth make sincere, informed, internally motivated, and committed decisions about their behavior. They help prepare young people so they can be successful with their decisions.

Potential Problems:

- Do not sufficiently help young people understand what is entailed in decisions about quitting drug use – what they give up; how hard it is to follow through; what it takes to be successful; what pressures will exist; the type of preparation required for success

- Allowing premature decisions. Get in a rush for decision-making – not able to defer or postpone discussions of decision-making (which should follow, not precede a full discussion of all relevant issues).

- Decisions about drug use are made without making important lifestyle decisions that go with it.

- Not enough emphasis on preparation for success.

RELAPSE PREVENTION / LIFESTYLE CHANGE

Goal: To help young people successfully follow through with their decisions; to cope with problems, mistakes and setbacks; to get support; and to constructively and supportively evaluate their own progress as they strive to make changes.

Potential Problems:

- Starting relapse prevention prematurely before decisions are sincere, firm, informed, internally motivated.

- Unrealistic expectations about change – without setbacks and mistakes.

- Failure to differentiate between lapse and relapse.

- Too harsh on setbacks.

- Does not tie in Challenge Two work on benefits of drug use in a powerful way in working on relapse prevention.

- Does not tie in Challenges Three and Five to developing a complete list of all the reasons to make changes – due to past, potential, and possible future harm from drug use.

- Not fully integrating Challenge Five to inspire optimism about the future.

- Not fully integrating Challenge Six to affirm decisions.

USE OF MATERIALS

INTRODUCTION TO MATERIALS

Goals: Published Seven Challenges materials introduced in a way that could potentially excite young people about using them. Preparing young people to use these resources well.

Potential Problems:

- The materials are not introduced with adequate finesse and enthusiasm.

- The posters are not displayed in counseling rooms.

- Pushing too hard, too soon: Not giving young people a chance to gradually adapt to the materials and come to appreciate them.

READINGS

Goals: Counselors use *The Seven Challenges* reader to help youth work through The Seven Challenges Process. Counselors use this resource fully by making sure that youth read pages relevant to the current discussions.

Potential Problems:

- Counselor not fully knowledgeable of readings in *The Seven Challenges*, so cannot fully integrate in day-to-day work with youth.

- Youth are not reading much; readings not incorporated in the program.

- Readings not being used during counseling sessions.

- Embarrassing youth who are not good readers.

- Inadequate screening of people with reading problems.

- Not enough help with reading for those with reading problems.

RESPONDING TO JOURNALS

Goals: Counselors use interactive journaling to help youth through The Seven Challenges Process; reinforcing interest and success with the process with positive comments. A special, journaling, written communication is established.

Potential Problems:

- Staff talks about "correcting" journals, not responding to them.

- The tone of comments are preachy, disapproving, harshly critical, harshly con-frontational, or argumentative.

- Insufficient feedback in journals (perhaps because of time pressures). (See Counselors not doing the required work, above, under Counselor Issues, page 132.)

- Clients not getting the feedback from adults and peers for questions that require this feedback.

- Staff members may try to "be nice" by simply signing pages of youths' journals without giving the "feedback from adults" that is required for that question.

- Superficial work is accepted without comment and request for completion.

- Youth are given more than one journal at a time.

- Feedback in journals sounds aggressively argumentative, or counselors trying to convert young people to their point of view with clever, but pushy comments.

- Harping on the dangers of drugs when youth are writing about the benefits.

- Not providing enough validation in journal responses.

- Feedback that does not fully embody the positive tone. It should be supportive, encouraging, expansive, and constructive.

- Youth giving good answers, but rushing through the journals. Counselors not slowing down the process.

- Counselors signing off on journals in which the work is incomplete.

- Counselors signing off on journals without passing them back and forth more than once.

- Youth have not read the corresponding chapter in *The Seven Challenges* before counselors sign off on the journal.

DEFICITS IN BASIC GROUP SKILLS

Goals: Creating a safe and supportive group; using group process, problem solving methods and activities to create a working environment in which young people can progress through The Seven Challenges. Counselors are attuned and responsive to the relevant issues and needs of individuals, and the entire group.

 The Seven Challenges Manual ©2004 Robert Schwebel, Ph.D.

Potential Problems:

- Serial one-to-ones with the leader (i.e., counselors interact with individual clients one at a time, without involving the group in the interactions).

- Not involving the *entire* group – all group members.

- Not making efforts to relate the experiences and work of individual group members to the work and experience of others.

- Groups are too rigidly planned; not responsive enough to the interests and needs of youth.

- Groups are too unstructured; not responsive enough to interests and needs of youth.

- Groups are not safe. Group leaders not protecting participants from abuse. They must have the ability to intervene and stop verbal attacks, or violation of other rules, should they occur.

- Counselor unable to establish and enforce rules.

- Counselor unable to "win the consciousness" (see Group Composition, pages 77-78) of the group.

- Fun and the work ethic: Even though we talk about a working group, in order to work as hard as we want young people to work in this program, the groups have to feel good. Problems occur when there is not enough time for fun and humor; when group members must sit still for too long and there is not enough active participation and physical movement.

- By taking a relaxing approach to group and striving for good feelings, some youth may see the program as an opportunity to "goof off" or misbehave. Although groups should have humor and be fun at times, it is a problem when group members use it as an opportunity to goof off or misbehave.

- Groups are not working groups (see just below).

WORKING SESSIONS

Goals: In a working session, youth will actively reflect upon their lives, engage in problem solving efforts, plan and implement behavior changes, or participate in structured activities.

Potential Problems:

- Working session never clearly defined.

- Counselor is not clear; many individuals or group members do not understand the concept of a "working session."

- Clients not taught how to work during sessions.

- Poorly planned groups due to insufficient effort in preparation/planning of sessions.

- Check-ins that do not end: Check-ins should be brief, and not incorporate problem solving. Sometimes distinction is blurred as one person's check-in merges into a problem solving session before everyone has had an opportunity to check in.

- Leaders not consistently sticking with the principle of insisting that sessions should be working sessions.

- Too much time is spent playing games or giving attention to negative behavior.

- Sessions are not responsive to youth and their issues.

ACTIVITIES

Goals: Activities are used to help clients identify personal issues, address problems, and learn skills. They are designed to help young people move through The Seven Challenges Process. Some activities are directly related to the drug issue. Others are related to other life problems, or designed to teach life and coping skills.

Potential Problems:

- Poorly planned activities.

- Activities without a clear beginning – youth are not adequately oriented to the purpose of the activity; activities started without explaining the purpose and connection to progress in the program; youth feel like passive recipients.

- Inflexibility in responding to issues that arise during the structured activities.

- Difficulty in sticking to activities; group is consistently sidetracked off task or distracted from focus.

- Not ending with a summary or some form of closure.

- Connections are not made and activities are not linked to challenges—Activities not integrated with The Seven Challenges Process

- Out of balance: Either activities are too focused on drugs issues (not enough focus on life skills and problem solving about life), or the opposite, not enough focus on drug issues.

- Counselors move ahead with activities without engaging youth. Kids are passive recipients.

APPENDIX ONE

SAMPLE SEVEN CHALLENGES GROUP NOTE

SEVEN CHALLENGES GROUP NOTE

NAME:_____ OBJECTIVE #:____ DATE OF GROUP:_____

IN THIS GROUP, YOUTH WORKED ON:

CLIMATE OF CHANGE
__ Establishing need for AOD group
__ Explaining and clarifying The Seven Challenges Process
__ Confronting barriers to group work
__ Issues related to peers in group
__ Dealing with issues of honesty and trust
__ Undoing negative expectations about counselors and treatment

MOTIVATING CHANGE
__ I.D. problems that motivate AOD use
__ I.D. needs met by drugs
__ Recognizing harm from AOD use
__ Acquiring information about AODs
__ Relating drug problems to other problems
__ Developing a future orientation
__ Exploring values
__ Identifying co-occurring problems
__ Participate in group activity

DECISION TO CHANGE
__ Seeing AODs as a lifestyle issue
__ Learning what it takes to change AOD use
__ Learning protective life skills
__ Dealing with problems that motivate AOD use
__ Addressing co-occurring problems
__ Plan behavior change

LIFESTYLE ACTION / RELAPSE PREVENTION
__ Identifying triggers
__ Anticipating and preparing for setbacks and mistakes
__ Developing relapse prevention plan
__ Implementing relapse prevention plan
__ Implement behavior change

SEVEN CHALLENGE SPECIFIC WORK
__ Issues related to *Seven Challenges Journal* work
__ Issues related to *The Seven Challenges* reading

INVOLVEMENT IN GROUP: 0 1 2 3 4
0 = not participating. 4 = excellent participation

APPROPRIATE BEHAVIOR: 0 1 2 3 4
0 = poor behavior. 4 = appropriate behavior

ASSESSMENT:

APPENDIX TWO

SAMPLE TREATMENT GOALS

FOR THE SEVEN CHALLENGES

TREATMENT GOALS FOR THE SEVEN CHALLENGES PROGRAM

CHALLENGE ONE

Because of difficulty being honest,..
Because of difficulty in self-disclosure,..
Because of problems of trust,..
Because of problems of trust with adults,..
Because of problems of trust with peers,..
Because of denial of problems,..

1. Identify and verbalize three barriers to honesty about AODs.
2. Identify and verbalize three barriers to honesty with peers in treatment.
3. Identify and verbalize barriers to honesty with counselor.
4. Identify three ways to increase trust so that honest therapeutic alliance can be built.
5. Openly and honestly disclose all AOD use to counselor.
6. Openly and honestly disclose all AOD use to group.
7. Identify barriers to being honest to him- or herself.
8. List five positive and five negative effects of drug use (in general, not on him or herself).
9. Accept feedback about drugs from adults.
10. Accept feedback about drugs from peers.
11. Read Chapter One in *The Seven Challenges*.
12. Complete Challenge One journaling.

CHALLENGE TWO

Because of lack of understanding of motivation for use of AOD problems...
Because of superficial understanding of motivation for use of AOD problems,..
Because is unaware of what needs are being met by use of AODs...
Because of self-blame about AOD problems,..

1. Verbalize why he or she has used drugs.
2. List five types of situations or specific feelings that have led to drug use.
3. List five situations that have led to drug use.
4. List three feelings that have preceded drug use.
5. Have a working definition of self-medication as evidenced by an ability to state how drugs have been used to change mood.
6. Have a working definition of escapism as evidenced by an ability to state how drugs have been used to try to avoid difficult situations.
7. Have an understanding of using drugs for courage as evidenced by being able to name three types of situations in which drugs were used to do things that were frightening.
8. List five benefits derived from using drugs.
9. List five needs that were met by using drugs.
10. Read Chapter Two in *The Seven Challenges*.
11. Complete Challenge Two journaling.

CHALLENGE THREE

Because of lack of understanding of harm from AOD use,..
Because of lack of understanding of potential harm from AOD use,..
Because has minimized harm from AOD use,..

Because has denied harm from AOD use,..
Because of limited ideas about the type of harm that can occur from drug abuse,..
Because has not understood that marijuana use can be harmful,..
Because has not understood that alcohol can be harmful,..
Because does not see how drug abuse has contributed to other problems in life,..

1. List five substantial ways in which he or she has been harmed by drug use.
2. List three ways that ___ (drug) is harmful.
3. Verbalize the difference between drug abuse and dependence.
4. List (X) ways that abusive (non-dependent) drug use can be harmful.
5. Identify (X) instances in life in which individual has used AODs abusively.
6. State characteristics of AOD dependence and verbally evaluate self in that context.
7. State five ways that drug use has been harmful in school.
8. ...harmful in family.
9. ...harmful in peer relations.
10. ...harmful at work.
11. ...harmful to self-esteem.
12. Explain potential harm from drugs, i.e., engaging in high-risk behavior which may or may not have already caused harm. Evaluate oneself in terms of potential harm from drugs.
13. Verbalize cost and consequences of drug use.
14. Read Chapter Three in *The Seven Challenges*.
15. Complete Challenge Three journaling.

CHALLENGE FOUR

Because does not realize how other problems have motivated drug abuse,..
Because does not see that life problems co-occur with drug problems and go together,...
Because does not understand that drug problems are lifestyle issues,..
Because of self-blaming tendency,...
Because of tendency to blame others for problems,...

1. Identify ways in which he or she has been harmed by others, or deprived of opportunities.
2. Be self-critical as evidenced by an ability to verbalize problems in himself or herself that he or she needs to work on.
3. List seven characteristics of the drug lifestyle.
4. List five problems that go with the drug lifestyle.
5. Understand constructive feedback as evidenced by an ability to (1) listen to constructive feedback from others and by an ability to (2) give constructive feedback to others.
6. Give constructive feedback to peers.
7. Accept constructive feedback from peers.
8. Identify and self-disclose (to peers, to self, in group) the following problems that co-occur with drug abuse:
   a. ...problems with peers
   b. ...problems with mood
   c. ...problems with anxiety
   d. ...problems with family
   e. ...trauma issues
   f. ...problems of low self-esteem
   g. ...deficits in problem solving skills
   h. ...problems in managing emotions
   i. ...problems in anger management

j.   ...deficit in ability to cope with difficult situations
k.   ...problems in impulse control
l.   ...deficit in communication skills
m.   ...acting out or anti-social behavior
9.   Read Chapter Four in *The Seven Challenges.*
10. Complete Challenge Four journaling.

CHALLENGE FIVE

Because lacking a future orientation,..
Because has not considered the impact of drug use upon his or her future,..
Because of a lack of a future vision,..
Because of hopelessness about the future,..
Because of a lack of a sense of self-efficacy,..

1.   Identify harm that is likely to occur if drug use continues at the current levels or increases.
2.   State three major goals for the long term future.
3.   List five short term goals and accomplish them.
4.   Break long term goal down into short term objectives, as demonstrated by a detailed plan to attain a single goal.
5.   List five benefits of a drug free lifestyle.
6.   Describe a drug free lifestyle.
7.   Describe a successful teenager who does not abuse AODs.
8.   Project effects of continued use of AODs at the level of use when treatment began, and write down what life would be like in one year and 10 years.
9.   Write a description of what you want your life to look like in 10 years.
10. List five characteristics of friends you want in the future.
11. Read Chapter Five in *The Seven Challenges.*
12. Complete Challenge Five journaling.

CHALLENGE SIX

Because of a need to *decide* to change harmful behavior and to make plans for change,..
Because of a need to change harmful behavior,..
Because of a need to plan for changes,..

1.   Do a written or verbal cost-benefit analysis of drug use, comparing benefits versus harm.
2.   Do a written or verbal cost-benefit analysis of continued lack of control of impulses (in other problem areas besides drugs).
3.   List five benefits that would be lost by stopping drug use.
4.   List 10 benefits of a drug free lifestyle.
5.   Know and be able to describe what it really means to him or herself to live a drug-free lifestyle. Include at least five changes this would involve.
6.   Develop and write down a plan for making new friends.
7.   Develop and write down a plan for managing anger.
8.   Develop and write down a plan for managing stress.
9.   Develop and write down a plan for controlling impulses.
10. Develop and write down a plan for coping with family problems and/or solving them.
11. Identify co-occurring problems and develop and write down a plan for resolving these problems.

12. Learn new communication skills and practice them in daily life.
13. Begin to socialize with non drug-using friends.
14. Identify situations that trigger drug use.
15. Identify thoughts that trigger drug use. Write powerful rebuttals.
16. Identify feelings that trigger drug use.
17. Write a contract with himself or herself as a commitment to stop abusing AOD.
18. Write a plan for changing AOD use.
19. Identify by name two trustworthy, supportive adults with whom you can talk, and talk with them.
20. Write a relapse prevention plan.
21. Make plans about how to respond to all triggers to avoid relapse.
22. Devise a plan for responding to urges to use drugs.
23. List new ways to have fun without drugs.
24. List resources for remaining drug-free.
25. Write a goodbye letter to drugs and share with group.
26. Share relapse prevention plan with family (or supportive adults) and ask for their support.
27. Read Chapter Six in *The Seven Challenges*.
28. Complete Challenge Six journaling.

CHALLENGE SEVEN

Because of a need to carry out plans for change and to avoid relapse,..
Because of the possibility of lapses,...

1. Be able to state the difference between lapse and relapse.
2. Develop a plan to prevent a lapse from becoming a relapse.
3. Participate in alternative activities.
4. Socialize with non-drug using friends.
5. Make non-drug-using friends.
6. Practice new communication skills.
7. Identify and express feelings appropriately.
8. Learn to sustain and gracefully terminate a conversation.
9. Introduce self to five new people.
10. Verbally weigh options and consider short term and long term consequences of behavior.
11. Problem solve about emotional predicaments.
12. Connect with at least one adult with whom youth can talk openly and honestly about everything.
13. Learn self-nurturing as evidenced by an ability to identify successes and learn from setbacks.
14. Build a supportive network of at least three people to resist pressure to relapse.
15. Use some form of relaxation exercise on a daily basis.
16. Communicate anger in a disciplined way.
17. Tolerate pain, sadness or frustration without using drugs.
18. Take social risks without using AODs.
19. Find and attend community recovery groups.
20. With guidance, successfully deal with increasingly higher risk situations (i.e., situations where drugs might be available).
21. Read Chapter Seven in *The Seven Challenges*.
22. Complete Challenge Seven journaling.

ENDNOTES

The Seven Challenges Manual   ©2004 Robert Schwebel, Ph.D.

ENDNOTES

1 Winters, K.C., Stinchfield, R.D, Opland, E., Weller, C., & Latimer, W.W. (2000). The effectiveness of the Minnesota Model approach in the treatment of adolescent drug abusers. *Addiction, 95,* 601-612.

2 Werner, E., & Smith, R. (1989). *Vulnerable but invincible: A longitudinal study of resilient children and youth.* New York: Adams, Bannister, and Cox. Also, Werner, E., & Smith, R. (1992). *Overcoming the odds: High-risk children from birth to adulthood.* New York: Cornell University Press.

3 Brehm, S.S., & Brehm, J.W. (1981) *Psychological reactance.* New York: Wiley.

4 Zautra, A.J. (2003). *Emotions, stress, and health.* NY: Oxford University Press.

5 Project MATCH Research Group (1997). Project MATCH secondary a priori hypotheses. *Addiction, 92,* 1671-1698. Also, Solomon K.E. and Annis, H.M. (1990). Outcome and efficacy expectancy in the prediction of post treatment drinking behaviour. *British Journal of Addiction, 85,* 659-665.

6 Shedler, J & Block, J., (1990). "Adolescent drug use and psychological health: A longitudinal inquiry." *American Psychologist, 45, No. 5,* 612-630.

7 Prochaska, J.O., DiClemente, C.C. & Norcross, J.C. (1992). In search of how people change. *American Psychologist, 47,* 1102-1114

8 Schwebel, R. (1998). *Saying NO is not enough: Helping your kids make wise decisions about alcohol, tobacco, and other drugs.* NY: Newmarket Press. Also, an enormous array of resources are available from the National Clearinghouse for Alcohol and Drug Information, 1-800-729-6686 or http://www.health.org.

9 Hser, Y.I., Grella, C.E., Hubbard, R.L., Hsieh, S.C., Fletcher, B.W., Brown, B.S. & Anglin, M.D. (2001). An evaluation of drug treatments for adolescents in four U.S. cities. *Archives of General Psychiatry, 58,* 689-695. Also, Craddock, S.G., Bray, R.M. and Hubbard, R.L. (1985). *Drug use before and during drug abuse treatment: 1979-1981 TOPS admission cohorts* (DHHS Publication No. (ADM) 85-1387). Rockville, MD: National Institute on Drug Abuse. Also, Hubbard, R.L., Cavanaugh, E.R., Craddock, S.G., and Rachal, J.V. (1985). Characteristics, behaviors, and outcomes for youth in the TOPS. In A.S. Friedman and G.M. Beschner (Eds.), *Treatment services for adolescent substance abusers* (pp 49-65). Rockville, MD: National Institute on Drug Abuse. Also, Office of Applied Studies (OAS) (1995). *Services Research Outcomes Study.* Rockville, MD: Substance Abuse and Mental Health Services Administration. (Available online at http://www.drugabusestatistics.samhsa.gov)

10 Schulman E.D. (1986). *Interventions in Human Services: A guide to skills and knowledge.* Columbus, Ohio: Merrill Publishing Company. Also: Corey, G. Corey M.S. & Callanan P. (1984). *Issues and ethics in the helping professions.* Belmont, CA: Brooks/Cole Publishing Company.

11 Truax, C.B. and Mitchell, K.M. (1971). Research on certain therapist interpersonal skills in relation to process and outcome. In A.E. Bergin & S.L. Garfield (Eds.) *Handbook of psychotherapy and behavior change: An empirical analysis* (pp. 299-344). New York: Wiley. Also, Truax, C.B. and Carkhuff R.R. (1967) *Toward effective counseling and psychotherapy.* Chicago: Aldine.

12 Prochaska, J.O., DiClemente, C.C. & Norcross, J.C. (1992). In search of how people change. *American Psychologist, 47,* 1102-1114

13 Dennis, M.L., Dawud-Noursi, S., Muck, R., & McDermeit, M. (2003). The need for developing and evaluating adolescent treatment models. In S.J. Stevens & A.R. Morral (Eds.), *Adolescent substance abuse treatment in the United States: Exemplary models from a national evaluation study* (pp. 3-34). Binghamton, NY: Haworth Press.

14 Najavits, Lisa M.(2002). *Seeking safety: A treatment manual for PTSD and substance abuse.* NY: The Guilford Press.

15 Murphy, S.L & Khantzian E.J. (1995). Addiction as a "self-medication" disorder: Application of ego psychology to the treatment of substance abuse. In A.M Washton (Ed.) *Psychotherapy and substance abuse: A practitioner's handbook* 161-175.

16 Schwebel, R. (1998). *Saying NO is not enough: Helping your kids make wise decisions about alcohol, tobacco, and other drugs.* NY: Newmarket Press.

17 Miller, W.R. & Rollnick S.R. (2002). *Motivational interviewing.* New York: The Guilford Press.

18 Bem, D.J. (1967). Self-perception: An alternative interpretation of cognitive dissonance phenomena. *Psychological Review, 74,* 183-200. Also, Bem (1972) Self-perception theory. In L. Berkowitz (Ed.), *Advances in Experimental Psychology (Vol. 6* pp. 1-62). New York: Academic Press p. 40.

19 Miller, W.R. & Rollnick S.R. (2002). *Motivational interviewing.* New York: The Guilford Press.

20 Marlatt, G.A. & Gordon, J.R. (Eds.) (1985). *Relapse prevention: Maintenance strategies in the treatment of addictive behaviors.* New York: Guilford Press. Also: Zackon, F, McAuliffe, & Ch'ien, J.M.N. (1993) *Recovery training and self-help: relapse prevention and aftercare for drug addicts.* U.S. Department of Health and Human Services. NIH Publication No. 93-3521. Also Gorski, T.T. and Miller M. (1986). *Staying Sober.* Independence, Missouri: Herald House.

21 Collins, R.L. (1997) Drinking restraint and risk for alcohol abuse. In Marlatt,.G.A. & VandenBos, G.R. *Addictive Behaviors: Readings on etiology, prevention, and treatment.* Washington, D.C. American Psychological Association pp. 289-306. Also, Marlatt, G.A., & Gordon, J.R. (1980). Determinants of relapse: Implications for the maintenance of behavior change. In P.O. Davidson and S.M. Davidson (Eds.) *Behavioral medicine: Changing health lifestyles* (pp.410-452). New York: Guilford Press.

22 Miller, W.R. & Rollnick S.R. (2002). *Motivational interviewing.* New York: The Guilford Press.

23 Berg, I. & Miller, S. (1992). *Working with the problem drinker: A solution-focused approach.* New York: Norton.

24 Schwebel, R. (1998). *Saying NO is not enough: Helping your kids make wise decisions about alcohol, tobacco, and other drugs.* NY: Newmarket Press.

25 Schwebel, R. (1994). *Who's on top, who's on bottom: How couples can learn to share power.* NY: Newmarket Press.

26 Miller, W.R. & Rollnick S.R. (2002). *Motivational interviewing.* New York: The Guilford Press.

27 Christoff, A. (2003). Personal communication at CSAT Drug Court Grantee Meeting, Washington, D.C., July, 12, 2003.

28 Simmons, R. (2002) *Odd girl out: The hidden culture of aggression in girls.* New York: Harcourt, Inc.

29 The Office of Juvenile Justice and Delinquency Prevention (1998). *Guiding principles for promising female programming: An inventory of best practices.* Washington D.C.: The Office of Juvenile Justice and Delinquency Prevention

30 Acoca, L. (1995). Breaking the cycle: A developmental model for the assessment and treatment of adolescents with alcohol and other drug problems. *Juvenile & Family Court Journal, 46(4),* 1-45. Addresses the issue raised by Carol Gilligan.

31 Hanson, G. R. (2003). "In drug abuse, gender matters." *NIDA Notes, 17, No. 2,* (pp. 3-4). Also, Associated Press (2003). "New addiction treatment targeted to girls, are urged" *The Arizona Daily Star,* February 6, 2003.

ABOUT THE AUTHOR

Robert Schwebel, Ph.D., is a psychologist who developed The Seven Challenges Program for adolescent drug treatment, now widely used across the United States, in Canada and Puerto Rico. He is the author of several books including *Saying No Is Not Enough: Helping Children Make Wise Decisions about Alcohol, Tobacco and Other Drugs* and *Keep Your Kids Tobacco-Free*. He also wrote *Who's on Top, Who's on Bottom: How Couples Can Learn to Share Power*. He has appeared on the Oprah Show, The Today Show, The CBS Early Show, CNN interviews and other national media. From 1998-2003 he answered parents' questions as the resident psychologist at Parentsoup.com of iVillage. In 2001, he wrote the booklet *Helping Your Children Navigate Their Teenage Years: A Guide for Parents* for the White House Council on Youth Violence. Dr. Schwebel gives keynote presentations, workshops, and training seminars to professionals and parents around the country. He lives with his wife and two children in Tucson, Arizona.

CONTACT INFORMATION

Dr. Schwebel can be contacted by email: rschwebel@sevenchallenges.com or by telephone at (520) 748-2122. His mailing address is c/o Viva Press, P.O. Box 57621, Tucson, AZ 85732.

WEBSITE

www.sevenchallenges.com